The Identification of Vat Dyes on Cellulosic Materials

The Identification of Vat Dyes on Cellulosic Materials

D. A. Derrett-Smith, B.Sc., F.R.I.C., F.T.I., F.S.D.C.
Formerly Director of the Linen Industry Research Association

and J. Gray, B.A., M.Sc., A.R.I.C.
Head of Bleaching, Dyeing, and Finishing Section
Linen Industry Research Association

PERGAMON PRESS

OXFORD · LONDON · EDINBURGH · NEW YORK
TORONTO · SYDNEY · PARIS · BRAUNSCHWEIG

Pergamon Press Ltd., Headington Hill Hall, Oxford
4 & 5 Fitzroy Square, London W.1
Pergamon Press (Scotland) Ltd., 2 & 3 Teviot Place, Edinburgh 1
Pergamon Press Inc., 44–01 21st Street, Long Island City, New York 11101
Pergamon of Canada, Ltd., 6 Adelaide Street East, Toronto, Ontario
Pergamon Press (Aust.) Pty. Ltd., 20–22 Margaret Street, Sydney, N.S.W.
Pergamon Press S.A.R.L., 24 rue des Écoles, Paris 5e
Vieweg & Sohn GmbH, Burgplatz 1, Braunschweig

First edition 1967

Library of Congress Catalog Card No. 66–27629

3015/67

CONTENTS

To enable users to keep this book up-to-date by adding details relating to new vat dyes, some blank tables (similar to those which appear on pages 12 to 77) are provided at the end of the text starting on page 110.

Chapter 1. INTRODUCTION

THE tables for the identification of vat dyes on cellulosic materials published in 1940 by Bradley and Derrett-Smith[1] and in 1947 by Derrett-Smith and Gee[2] were brought up to date in 1956 by Derrett-Smith and Gray.[3] These tables of British, German, Swiss vat dyes have now been completely revised. New dyes have been added, obsolete dyes have been omitted, and changes in the dye manufacturers' nomenclature have been incorporated. Each group of "synonymous" dyes has been given its colour index number.

In addition to the determination of the dyeing class of all the dyes commonly found on cellulosic materials, a new method of distinguishing between reactive and other classes of dyes on these materials has been included.

The arrangement of the dyes in the tables of characteristics has been based on the point of view of an investigator, who, having determined the characteristics of an unknown vat dye, wishes to find the dye in the tables as rapidly as possible. The tables have been arranged as far as possible so that dyes with the same characteristics are grouped together; dyes with only slight differences in characteristics are put adjacent to each other. It is therefore an easy matter to find the place of an unknown dye in the tables, and it can be seen at a glance which dyes it resembles. Synonymous commercial products have been grouped together in alphabetical order.

It is not claimed that any vat dye can be identified completely by means of these tables alone. They have been prepared with the primary object of providing a rapid "sorting-out" test. For the complete identification of a particular dye it is then necessary to compare its characteristics with those of sample dyeings of the dyes which it resembles. Such sample dyeings are provided in the manufacturers' pattern cards.

In previous publications [4–12] the dyes have generally been arranged in accordance with the manufacturers' names, but the advantage from a practical point of view of arranging the dyes according to their characteristics is an obvious one.

Five reagents have been employed, viz. alkaline and acid solutions of sodium hydrosulphite, concentrated nitric and sulphuric acids and acid solution of potassium permanganate. Other workers have employed reagents such as pyridine or benzene which are solvents for some vat dyes, and also hypochlorite solutions and acid stannous chloride solutions, whilst Herzog[11] employed only alkaline and acid solutions of sodium hydrosulphite and concentrated sulphuric acid. In the present work it has been found that the five reagents are all necessary, and are sufficient for the identification of all vat dyes, with the exception of certain black and blue dyes, for the identification of which additional tests are provided (see p. 82 and Chapters 5 and 6).

The terminology used in describing the characteristics of the dyes has been curtailed as much as possible for the sake of clarity. Such terms as "pale", "dark", "very dull", "brilliant", "reddish", and "bluish" have been avoided. Terms such as "no variation", "unchanged", and "discharged" have not been used, the colour obtained in every case being described. It is considered that many of the terms and abbreviations of terms used in earlier papers are better avoided.

The present work refers only to reactions for the identification of vat dyes, and it is a necessary preliminary to determine the type of dye under examination before making use of the tables (see Chapter 4).

The code letters used for indicating the names of the various dye manufacturers' are as follows:

Badische Anilin & Soda Fabrik A.G.	BASF
Cassella Farbwerke, Mainkur A.G.	CFM
Ciba Ltd.	CIBA
Durand & Huguenin S.A.	DH
Farbenfabriken Bayer A.G.	FBy
Farbwerke Hoechst A.G.	FH
Geigy Co. Ltd.	Gy
Imperial Chemical Industries Ltd.	ICI
L.B. Holliday & Co. Ltd.	LBH
Sandoz Ltd.	S
Yorkshire Dyeware & Chemical Co. Ltd.	YDC

REFERENCES

1. BRADLEY, H. B., and DERRETT-SMITH, D. A., *J.S.D.C.*, **56**, 97 (1940).
2. DERRETT-SMITH, D. A., and GEE, B. C., *J.S.D.C.*, **63**, 401 (1947).
3. DERRETT-SMITH, D. A., and GRAY, J., *J.S.D.C.*, **72**, 211 (1956).
4. HOLDEN, G. E., *J.S.D.C.*, **25**, 41 (1909).
5. GREEN, A. G. and FRANK, G. H., *J.S.D.C.*, **26**, 83 (1910).
6. BUDE, R., *Melliand Textilber.*, 1924, **5**, 602.
7. JONES, J. and KILBY, W., *J.S.D.C.*, **41**, 127 (1925).
8. VAJS, M., *Melliand Textilber.*, 1927, **8**, 611.
9. SCHULTZ, G., *Farbstofftabellen*, 7th edition, 1927.
10. 'Anthragoid', *Amer. Dyestuff Rep.*, 1931, **20**, 65.
11. HERZOG, E., *Reactionstabelle der Küpenfarbstoffe* (Wepf et Cie.), 1933.
12. BORGHETTY, H. C. and BRODEN, K. J., *Amer. Dyestuff Rep.*, 1937, **26**, 589.

Apart from the introduction of new dyes the manufacturers are constantly adding to and subtracting from their ranges of vat and soluble vat dyes. It is likely therefore that at the time of publication a number of dyes may not be available under certain of the commercial names listed. For example Ciba Ltd., Geigy Co. Ltd., and Sandoz Ltd. have recently ceased marketing soluble vat dyes, and the Cibacron, Tinosol and Sandozol ranges accordingly are no longer available.

These and other dyes which have been withdrawn are available under other commercial names listed in the tables.

Chapter 2. DETAILS OF THE TESTS

METHODS of preparing the five reagents used in the tests are as follows:

I. Alkaline Hydrosulphite. 25 g sodium hydrosulphite are dissolved in 500 ml cold 2 per cent (wt/vol.) caustic soda solution.

II. Acid Hydrosulphite. (a) 50 g "Formosul" (sodium sulphoxylate–formaldehyde) are dissolved in 500 ml warm water, and the solution allowed to cool.

(b) 2 ml glacial acetic acid are diluted to 500 ml with water.

Equal proportions of solutions (a) and (b) are employed as acid hydrosulphite. The solutions should be kept in separate bottles until required.

The reagents described above are best kept in 500 ml rubber-stoppered bottles.

III. Nitric Acid. This is concentrated nitric acid (analytical reagent). S.G. = 1·42.

IV. Sulphuric Acid. This is concentrated sulphuric acid (analytical reagent). S.G. = 1·84.

V. Acid Potassium Permanganate and Acid Hydrogen Peroxide.

(a) *Acid potassium permanganate.* 10 g potassium permanganate are dissolved in 400 ml water and 100 ml of normal sulphuric acid are added.

(b) *Acid hydrogen peroxide.* 25 ml of 100 vol. hydrogen peroxide are mixed with 425 ml water and 50 ml normal sulphuric acid are added.

TEST I

Alkaline Hydrosulphite. A small sample of the dyed material under examination is placed in a test tube and about 5 ml reagent added. The solution is boiled for 2–3 sec and the change in colour of the sample observed. All vat dyeings are "vatted" by this treatment, i.e. the sodium salt of the leuco compound is obtained. The colour of the "vat", as stated in the manufacturers' pattern cards, refers to the solution of the alkali salt of the leuco compound. In this work the colour of the vat refers to the colour observed on the fibre. Except in the case of a few very deep shades it is not necessary to boil for longer than 2–3 sec. With the majority of vat dyes the colour of the sodium leuco compound is distinct from that of the dyed shade, though certain types of blue vat dyes provide exceptions. Dyes of the same shade often give differently coloured leuco compounds. For example, Caledon Gold Orange GN and Caledon Gold Orange 3G are almost indistinguishable in shade, but the former gives a blue–red "vat", and the latter a brown "vat". As these two dyes differ in properties, e.g. the former accelerates the tendering action of hypochlorite solutions on cellulose in the presence of light, whilst the latter is much less active in this respect, the value of a simple distinguishing test is evident.

The alkaline hydrosulphite reagent may be kept for long periods without serious deterioration in reducing power, except when the stock-bottle is almost empty. It is advisable to test the reducing power of the reagent before use, by means of a full shade of Indanthren Rubine R which is comparatively difficult to "vat", and if the green–blue leuco compound is not obtained on boiling in the reagent for 2–3 sec, the solution should be rejected and a fresh stock prepared.

TEST II

Acid Hydrosulphite. The procedure is similar to that described for Test I, approximately equal proportions of Formosul and acetic acid stock solutions being used.

The colour change of the material in this test is due to the formation of the free leuco compound of the dye, which in many cases has a colour different from that of the alkaline "vat" or the original dyed shade, e.g. Caledon Grey 3B gives a blue alkaline "vat" and a brown–red free leuco compound in acid hydrosulphite. Although it is usually necessary in this test to boil only for 2–3 sec as in Test I, it is advisable as a general rule to boil for about 10 sec in order to obtain the colour change on the fibre. Some dyes, particularly dyes of the indigoid type, are decolorized or stripped to a greater or less degree. Such stripping frequently involves a gradual series of colour changes, e.g. Indanthren Printing Violet BBF changes to blue–grey and then to green–yellow.

Valuable evidence may often be obtained by prolonging the boiling and observing the stages through which the colour passes.

As in Test I, it is advisable to test the reducing power of the reagent before use if it has been kept for some time, and for Test II a full shade of Caledon Jade Green XN is recommended. The blue–red colour of the free leuco compound should be obtained on boiling in the reagent for 10 sec.

TEST III

Nitric Acid. This reagent is used cold. About 5–10 ml are poured into a clean, dry, white porcelain dish and a sample of the dyed material immersed in the acid. Many vat dyes are readily oxidized by nitric acid, and characteristic colour changes occur, e.g Caledon Blue XRN changes immediately to yellow, and many green dyes are oxidized to black. The colour change on the fibre usually occurs immediately, although in some cases a gradual series of colour changes may be observed and these afford additional evidence. In a few cases, although little change in colour of the sample appears to occur, oxidation products of the dye begin to bleed away from the sample into the acid which becomes characteristically coloured, e.g. Indanthren Grey M and Indanthren Grey MG are indistinguishable in all four tests, except for the fact that in nitric acid after about 30 sec immersion, the former bleeds a green–blue colour and the latter a violet colour. It is therefore necessary to observe the behaviour of a sample in the acid for 15–30 sec.

Nitric acid is a valuable reagent for distinguishing members of certain families of dyes where these members resemble each other very closely in chemical constitution; the indigo and the indanthrone blue families are examples. Both are made by increasing halogenation of the parents indigo and indanthrone. Distinctions which can be made within these two groups are described in Chapters 5 and 6.

The nitric acid must be colourless and is preferably kept in a dark bottle, otherwise it becomes yellow and this can obscure the colour changes.

TEST IV

Sulphuric Acid. This reagent is also used cold. The dyed sample is immersed in 5–10 ml of the acid in a white porcelain dish. All vat dyes are soluble in concentrated sulphuric acid, although some are much more soluble than others and a few dissolve only with difficulty. As in Test III, the behaviour of a sample in the acid should be observed for at least 15–30 sec. Care is necessary in making observations in this test. As the dye begins to dissolve away from the fibre, the acid round the sample becomes coloured. If the dish is kept stationary during the test, the coloured solution diffuses outwards and downwards from the sample, and this colour, apart from that of the sample, can then clearly be seen. For example, Durindone Scarlet 2B and Durindone Scarlet 3B are indistinguishable in all four tests, except for the fact that, after 15–30 sec immersion in sulphuric acid, the former bleeds a blue colour, and the latter a green colour.

In the tables of characteristics the colour of the solution of the dye in sulphuric acid has been recorded. In cases where this colour is distinctly different from the colour of the dyed material, the latter also has been stated, e.g. with Indanthren Yellow 7GK the solution and sample are both red, whilst with Indanthren Yellow G the solution is red, but the sample remains substantially yellow. With full shades of dark blues and blacks the sample appears black, although the solution may show another colour.

The sulphuric acid must be kept in a bottle with a well-fitting glass stopper, as otherwise it readily absorbs moisture. The specific gravity must be 1·84 otherwise the correct colour may not be obtained.

TEST V

Acid Potassium Permanganate and Acid Hydrogen Peroxide. A sample of the dyed material is placed in a portion of solution (a) in a small basin, and thoroughly wetted out. After 2 min immersion, the sample is removed, rinsed in water, and placed in solution (b) until the brown stain is removed. This is usually completed in about 30 sec, after which the sample is removed, rinsed, transferred to white absorbent paper, and examined. Colour comparisons should be made within a reasonably short time of carrying out the test, since on prolonged exposure to air some of the colours are liable to alteration, especially in the case of indanthrone blue dyes. The use of acid hydrogen peroxide as a clearing bath is preferred to acid sodium sulphite since the latter causes some reversion towards the original shade, particularly when used with indanthrone blue dyeings.

The colour changes produced by applying the reagent to red, orange, yellow, and brown dyeings are slight, and provide little useful information.

As described in Chapters 5 and 6, blue dyes derived from indanthrone can be distinguished by treatment with nitric acid of various strengths. Similar distinctions can be made with acidified permanganate, the colours obtained with this reagent ranging from green–yellow to green–blue depending on the chlorine fastness of the blue dye.

POINTS TO BE OBSERVED IN MAKING THE TESTS

Apart from the details given regarding the preparation and use of the five reagents, there are several points to be noted.

Dyeings on Various Cellulosic Materials. Several vat dyes on boiled cotton, bleached linen, and viscose rayon materials, have been examined and no differences in the test results have been observed. With dyeings on linen materials made from boiled yarns, non-cellulosic substances present in the yarn do not vitiate the tests.

Dyeings on Yarn and Cloth. The majority of the dyes examined were dyed on yarn. With piece dyeings or prints it is advisable to pick out the threads from the cloth, particularly for Tests III, IV, and V, which are carried out cold, otherwise the reagents do not penetrate readily into the sample and an incorrect observation may be made. Even in Tests I and II, deep shades on cloth of some dyes having a relatively high resistance to reduction, require a rather longer period of boiling than is generally necessary.

Size of Sample. Only small samples of the dyed material under examination are required for each test, ½–1 in. of yarn or ¼ in. square of cloth being ample. The use of larger samples does not facilitate the tests.

Depth of Shade. The dyes examined were in medium or full shades. It has been observed in several cases that the colour changes obtained with pale and deep shades of the same dye in the same test are not exactly the same. In examining pale shades allowance must be made for this fact in interpreting the characteristics as defined in the tables. In certain cases, however, distinctions are evident in pale shades which are obscured in deeper shades of the same dyes, e.g. Caledon Orange 2RT and Caledon Brilliant Orange 4RN.

Comparison of Dyeings with Standard Shades. Having determined the characteristics of a dyeing in the four tests and having found in the tables the dye or dyes which the unknown resembles, the final criterion of the identification is to compare with standard dyeings. Cases have been found where the shade of the dyeing under examination was not identical with the reference dyeing of the vat dye it appeared to be. Certain factors can account for these discrepancies in shade. These are:

(i) The presence of small quantities of other dyes used for shading purposes in the material under examination.
(ii) The efficiency with which a dyeing has been soaped-off after dyeing.
(iii) The moisture content of the dyed material.
(iv) Deterioration of the reference shade on storage.

A discrepancy in shade due to (ii), (iii), or (iv), as evidence disagreeing with the findings of the four tests, may be neglected, i.e. the colour changes observed in the tests are more reliable than considerations of the exact shade of the dyeing. In the case of (i) above, the presence of a small quantity of another vat dye would probably give rise to some discrepancies in the colour changes in the tests. An additional test for this is given in Chapter 4, p. 83. The presence of a direct dye as shading colour may also be detected (see Chapter 4, p. 84).

Mixture Shades. The present tables have been prepared for the identification of dyeings of individual vat dyes, which is a necessary preliminary to attempting the identification of the components of a mixture of two or more vat dyes. The presence of more than one vat dye generally leads to difficulties in identification tests. Up to the present there is no universally applicable procedure for this purpose. The difficulties arise from the fact that in dyeing shades which necessitate the use of two or more vat dyes in admixture, the dyer must exercise care in selecting dyes which resemble each other as closely as possible in vatting, dyeing, exhaustion, and fastness properties. Consequently, the better the choice of dyes made by the dyer, the less are the chances of being able to separate and identify the component dyes. As the present tables have been made as completely up-to-date as possible, it may be concluded that a vat dyeing which shows characteristics incapable of being regarded as similar to those of any dye in the tables, must be a mixture. When one component dye is present in a large proportion and the other component or components present in very small proportions, the characteristics of the mixture may be only slightly different from those of the major component, and sufficient evidence may be obtained to deduce the identity of the latter. In the case of mixtures of badly chosen dyes, where pronounced differences in vatting properties may exist, some degree of separation may be possible by the additional test already mentioned (see Chapter 4).

Arrangement of the Dyes in the Tables. The dyes have been classified in seven separate tables according to their nominal colour, thus:

Table I. Yellow and orange dyes.
Table II. Red dyes.
Table III. Violet dyes.
Table IV. Blue dyes.
Table V. Green dyes.
Table VI. Brown dyes.
Table VII. Grey and black dyes.

With any such classification border-line cases always occur, e.g. Caledon Dark Blue 2RD, Caledon Khaki R, Indanthren Red Brown 5RF and Indanthren Blue Green FFB may be considered to give almost violet, brown, red, and green shades respectively, but have been classified as nominally blue, green, brown, and blue dyes respectively.

Within each table the dyes have been arranged according to the colour of the alkaline "vat" in the following order: red–violet, violet, blue, green, yellow, red, brown, grey, and black.

Dyes which are identical and which therefore give the same colour reactions in the tests are grouped together. Beside each dye or group of synonymous dyes is given the colour index number.

Terminology Used. The number of terms employed in describing the colour changes observed in the tests has been limited as far as possible for the sake of clarity, and the terminology is outlined below.

Green–yellow
Yellow
Red–yellow
Brown–yellow

Red–violet
Violet

Blue
Green–blue

Yellow–green
Green
Blue –green
Brown–green

Yellow–red
Red
Blue–red
Brown–red

Yellow–brown
Brown
Red–brown
Green–brown

Grey
Black

In the compound terms used, e.g. "yellow–green" and "green–yellow", the first part qualifies the latter part, i.e. "yellow–green" is predominantly green, whilst "green–yellow" is predominantly yellow.

In view of the minimization of the number of colour terms used, the latter are not to be regarded as referring to specific hues, but as covering a narrow range of shades within the scope of each particular term. Thus "yellow–red", for instance, may refer to a number of compound shades composed of yellow and red in which the latter predominates. The designations used are considered sufficient to differentiate the colour reactions obtained in any given group of dyes.

In the case of the terms "grey" and "black", it is necessary to use qualifications such as "brown–grey", "green–grey", and "blue–black", "red–black", "brown–black", as with the primary colours. With all the other terms given above the qualifications "grey" and "black" have been used to describe "dullness" and "depth", respectively. For example, a flat, dull yellow has been termed "grey–yellow"; navy blue and bordeaux have been termed "black–blue" and "black–blue–red" respectively. The variety of terms used in previous publications of tables such as "dirty", "flat", "brilliant", have been avoided. Only such terms as were found to be necessary to describe adequately the differences in colour observed have been employed; e.g. "orange", "purple", "olive", "khaki", are not required.

A complete index of all the dyes included in the tables is given on pages 91–109.

TABLE I. *Yellow and Orange Dyes*

No.	Colour index	Dye	Alkaline hydrosulphite	Acid hydrosulphite	Nitric acid	Sulphuric acid	Acid permanganate
			Blue–red or red–violet				
5	Orange 1	Anthrasol Golden Yellow IRK Benzadone Gold Yellow RK Cibanone Golden Yellow FRK Cibantine Golden Yellow FRK Estersol Golden Yellow IRK Indanthren Golden Yellow RK Indigosol Golden Yellow IRK(F) Paradone Golden Yellow RK Sandothrene Golden Yellow F-NRK Sandozol Golden Yellow F-RK Soledon Golden Yellow RK Tinon Golden Yellow RK-F Tinosol Golden Yellow RK-F	Blue–red	Red–yellow	Red–yellow	Violet	–
10	Orange 9	Benzadone Gold Orange G Caledon Gold Orange GN Cibanone Golden Orange FG Indanthren Golden Orange G Paradone Golden Orange G Sandothrene Golden Orange F-NG Tinon Golden Orange G-F	Blue–red	Red–yellow	Brown–yellow	Blue	–

No.	Colour index	Dye	Alkaline hydrosulphite	Acid hydrosulphite	Nitric acid	Sulphuric acid	Acid permanganate
15	Yellow 44	Indanthren Printing Yellow GOW	Red–violet	Red–yellow	Red–yellow	Blue	–
20	Orange 4	Benzadone Brilliant Orange 4R Caledon Brilliant Orange 4RN Cibanone Orange F8R Indanthren Orange 4R Indigosol Orange I8R(F) Sandothrene Red Orange F-NR Sandozol Orange F-8R Tinon Orange 8R-F Tinosol Orange 8R-F	Red–violet	Brown–red	Brown–red	Blue	–
25	Orange 2	Benzadone Orange 2RT Caledon Orange 2RT Cibanone Golden Orange F2R Cibantine Golden Orange F2R Indanthren Orange RRTS Indigosol Golden Orange I2R(F) Paradone Orange RRT Sandothrene Red Orange F-NG Sandozol Golden Orange F-2R Tinon Golden Orange 2R-F Tinosol Golden Orange 2RL-F	Red–violet	Brown–red	Brown–red	Blue	–

No.	Colour index	Dye	Alkaline hydrosulphite	Acid hydrosulphite	Nitric acid	Sulphuric acid	Acid permanganate
30	Orange 22	Caledon Printing Yellow GW Cibanone Golden Yellow FGW Paradone Golden Yellow GW Sandothrene Golden Yellow F-NGW Tinon Golden Yellow GW-F	Grey–red–violet *Violet*	Brown–yellow	Red–yellow	Brown	–
35	Yellow 2	Anthra Yellow GC Caledon Yellow 5G Cibanone Yellow GC Paradone Yellow GC Paradone Yellow GCX Sandothrene Yellow NGC Tinon Yellow GC	Violet	Red–yellow	Green–yellow	Green–yellow	–
40	Orange 19	Cibanone Brilliant Orange FGK Indanthren Brilliant Orange GK Sandothrene Brilliant Orange F-NGK Tinon Brilliant Orange GK-F	Violet	Red–yellow	Red–yellow	Yellow–green	–
45	Orange 3	Anthrasol Brilliant Orange IRK Caledon Brilliant Orange 6R Caledon Printing Orange 6R Cibanone Brilliant Orange FRK					

No.	Colour index	Dye	Alkaline hydrosulphite	Acid hydrosulphite	Nitric acid	Sulphuric acid	Acid permanganate
		Cibantine Brilliant Orange FRK Indanthren Brilliant Orange RK Indanthren Brilliant Orange RKN Indanthren Brilliant Orange RKS Indigosol Brilliant Orange IRK(F) Paradone Brilliant Orange RK Sandothrene Brilliant Orange F-NRK Sandozol Brilliant Orange F-RK Soledon Brilliant Orange 6R Tinon Brilliant Orange RK-F Tinosol Brilliant Orange RK-F	Violet	Red–yellow	Yellow–red	Yellow–green	–
50	Yellow 46	Indanthren Yellow 5GF	Violet (blue–red solution)	Brown–red	Yellow (stripped)	Green–yellow	–
55	Orange 16	Indanthren Orange F3R	Black–violet	Brown–yellow	Red–yellow	Red–yellow	–
60	Yellow 7	Anthrasol Yellow V Cibantine Yellow V					

No.	Colour index	Dye	Alkaline hydrosulphite	Acid hydrosulphite	Nitric acid	Sulphuric acid	Acid permanganate
		Indigosol Yellow V Sandozol Yellow V Tinosol Yellow V	Black–violet	Green–yellow	Green–yellow	Brown–yellow	–
			Blue				
65	Yellow 1	Caledon Yellow GN Cibanone Yellow FGN Indanthren Yellow G Paradone Yellow G New Sandothrene Yellow F-NG Sandothrene Yellow F–NGN Tinon Yellow GN-F	Blue	Black–green–blue	Red–yellow	Red–yellow	–
			Green				
70	Orange 7	Indanthren Brilliant Orange GR Paradone Brilliant Orange GR New	Yellow–green	Black–green	Red–yellow	Red–yellow	–
75	–	Indanthren Brilliant Orange RR	Green	Green	Yellow–red	Yellow–brown	–
80	Yellow 13	Caledon Yellow 4G Paradone Yellow 4G	Blue–green	Yellow	Yellow	Red–yellow	–
85	Yellow 12	Indanthren Yellow 3G Indanthren Yellow 3GFN	Grey–green	Yellow	Green–yellow	Brown–green then Black–brown	–

No.	Colour index	Dye	Alkaline hydrosulphite	Acid hydrosulphite	Nitric acid	Sulphuric acid	Acid permanganate
90	Yellow 14	Cibanone Yellow FLGR Sandothrene Yellow F-NLGR Tinon Yellow LGR-F	Grey–green *Yellow*	Yellow	Yellow	Yellow–brown	–
95	Orange 5	Algol Orange RF Anthrasol Orange HR Ciba Orange R Cibantine Orange R Durindone Orange R Indigosol Orange HR Sandothrene Orange R Sandozol Orange R Soledon Orange R Tinosol Orange R Tina Orange R	Green–yellow	Yellow–red	Yellow–red	Violet	–
100	Yellow 5	Anthrasol Yellow HCG Indigosol Yellow HCGN Sandozol Yellow CG Tinosol Yellow CG	Green–yellow (stripped)	Green–yellow	Brown–yellow	Red–violet	–
105	Yellow 24	Cibanone Yellow 2GR Sandothrene Yellow N2GR Tinon Yellow 2GR	Red–yellow	Green–yellow	Green–yellow	Yellow	–
110	Orange 18	Cibanone Orange 6R Sandothrene Orange N6R Tinon Orange 6R	Red–yellow	Yellow	Red–yellow	Red	–

No.	Colour index	Dye	Alkaline hydrosulphite	Acid hydrosulphite	Nitric acid	Sulphuric acid	Acid permanganate
			Red				
115	Orange 11	Anthrasol Yellow I3R Caledon Yellow 3R Cibanone Yellow F3R Cibanone Yellow F3RF Indanthren Yellow 3R Indanthren Yellow 3RT Paradone Yellow 3RT Sandothrene Yellow F-N3R Soledon Yellow 3R Tinon Yellow 3R-F	Yellow–red	Grey–green–yellow	Red–yellow	Black–violet	–
120	Red 48	Indanthren Orange 7RK	Yellow–red	Yellow–brown	Brown–red	Grey–green	–
125	Orange 6	Indigosol Golden Yellow AR	Yellow–red	Red–yellow	Red–yellow	Red–yellow	–
130	Yellow 4	Anthrasol Golden Yellow GK Anthrasol Printing Yellow IGOK Benzadone Gold Yellow GK Caledon Golden Yellow GK Caledon Printing Yellow GK Cibanone Golden Yellow FGK Cibantine Golden Yellow FGK Indanthren Printing Yellow GOK Indigosol Golden Yellow IGK(F)	Red	Yellow	Red–yellow	Red–violet	–

No.	Colour index	Dye	Alkaline hydrosulphite	Acid hydrosulphite	Nitric acid	Sulphuric acid	Acid permanganate
		Paradone Golden Yellow GK Sandothrene Golden Yellow NGK Sandozol Golden Yellow F-GK Soledon Golden Yellow GK Tinon Golden Yellow GK Tinosol Golden Yellow GK-F					
135	Yellow 29	Indanthren Yellow 7GK	Grey–red	Red–yellow	Yellow	Red–yellow	–
140	Yellow 31	Indanthren Yellow 4GK	Grey–red	Yellow	Red–yellow	Yellow	–
145	Yellow 26	Benzadone Yellow 5GK Caledon Yellow 5GK Cibanone Yellow F5GK Indanthren Yellow 5GK Indanthren Printing Yellow 5GK Paradone Yellow 5GK Sandothrene Yellow F-N5GK Tinon Yellow 5GK	Black–red	Green–yellow	Green–yellow	Yellow	–
150	Yellow 6	Indigosol Yellow R(F) Sandozol Yellow F-R Tinosol Yellow R-F	Brown–red	Green–yellow	Yellow	Brown–yellow	–
155	Yellow 47	Anthrasol Printing Yellow 4G	Brown–red (stripped)	Yellow–red	Yellow	Yellow–red	–

No.	Colour index	Dye	Alkaline hydrosulphite	Acid hydrosulphite	Nitric acid	Sulphuric acid	Acid permanganate
			Brown				
160	Yellow 27	Caledon Printing Yellow 6G Indanthren Yellow 6GD Indanthren Yellow 6GK Indanthren Printing Yellow 6G	Yellow–brown	Grey–green	Yellow	Yellow–red	–
165	Orange 12	Caldeon Yellow 2R	Yellow–brown	Brown	Yellow	Yellow–brown then Blue	–
170	Yellow 20	Indanthren Yellow 4GF Paradone Yellow 4GF Paradone Yellow 8GF	Yellow–brown	Yellow–brown	Yellow	Brown–yellow	–
175	Orange 15	Caledon Gold Orange 3G Cibanone Golden Orange F3G Indanthren Golden Orange 3G Sandothrene Golden Orange F-N3G Tinon Golden Orange 3G-F	Brown	Brown–yellow	Red–yellow	Green–blue	–
180	–	Caledon Yellow Brown 3G Indanthren Yellow Brown 3G	Brown	Brown–yellow	Red–yellow	Green–blue	–
185	Orange 10	Sandothrene Golden Orange N2GT Tinon Golden Orange 2GT	Red–brown	Brown–yellow	Red–yellow	Green–yellow	–
190	Yellow 23	Caledon Yellow 4GL					

No.	Colour index	Dye	Alkaline hydrosulphite	Acid hydrosulphite	Nitric acid	Sulphuric acid	Acid permanganate
		Cibanone Yellow F2G Indanthren Yellow F3GG Sandothrene Yellow F-N2G	Violet–brown	Yellow	Brown	Red	–
195	Yellow 45	Cibantine Yellow F2G Indigosol Yellow I2G(F) Sandozol Yellow F-2G Tinosol Yellow 2G-F	Violet–brown	Yellow	Brown	Red	–
200	Yellow 10	Indanthren Yellow GGF Indanthren Yellow GGFP Indanthren Yellow GGFS	*Black* Grey	Yellow	Red–brown	Red	–
205	Yellow 37	Indanthren Yellow F2GC Indanthren Yellow F2GCS	Violet–grey	Yellow	Red–brown	Blue–red	–
210	Yellow 3	Cibanone Yellow FGK Indanthren Yellow GK Indigosol Yellow 2GB(F) Sandothrene Yellow F–NGKF Sandozol Yellow F–2GB Tinon Yellow GK–F Tinosol Yellow 2GB–F	Red–grey	Yellow	Yellow	Grey–yellow	–
215	Orange 13	Indanthren Orange RR	Black	Red–yellow	Red–yellow	Yellow	–

No.	Colour index	Dye	Alkaline hydrosulphite	Acid hydrosulphite	Nitric acid	Sulphuric acid	Acid permanganate
220	Orange 26	Indanthren Golden Orange GG	Black	Red–yellow	Yellow	Yellow	–
225	Yellow 23	Cibanone Yellow 2GW Sandothrene Yellow N2GW Tinon Yellow 2GW	Blue–black	Red–yellow	Yellow	Red–yellow	–
230	Yellow 30	Cibanone Yellow F2GK Sandothrene Yellow F–N2GK Tinon Yellow 2GK–F	Blue–black	Yellow	Yellow	Yellow	–
235	Orange 17	Indanthren Orange GG	Blue–black	Yellow	Red–yellow	Brown (on fibre) bleeds Red	–

TABLE II. *Red Dyes*

No.	Colour index	Dye	Alkaline hydrosulphite	Acid hydrosulphite	Nitric acid	Sulphuric acid	Acid permanganate
			Blue–red or Red–violet				
240	Red 23	Caledon Red 2GN Indanthren Red GG	Blue–red	Brown–red	Brown–red	Blue–red	–
245	Red	Caledon Red BN Cibanone Red FRK Indanthren Red RK Sandothrene Red F-N2R Tinon Red RK-F	Grey–blue–red	Brown–yellow	Yellow–red	Red–yellow	–
250	Red 49	Cibanone Copper Red FR Sandothrene Copper Red F-NR Tinon Copper Red R-F	Black–blue–red	Yellow–brown	Yellow–red	Brown	–
255	Red 45	Ciba Scarlet FG Durindone Scarlet Y Indanthren Printing Scarlet GG Tetra Scarlet F-G Tina Scarlet G-F	Red–violet	Yellow–red (stripped)	Red	Green	–
260	Red 29	Indanthren Scarlet R	Red–violet	Brown–red	Red	Blue	–
265	Red 55	Indanthren Brilliant Scarlet E3G	Red–violet	Red	Red	Red–violet	–

No.	Colour index	Dye	Alkaline hydrosulphite	Acid hydrosulphite	Nitric acid	Sulphuric acid	Acid permanganate
			Violet				
270	Red 37	Indanthren Scarlet GK Paradone Scarlet GK	Violet	Brown–yellow	Red	Yellow–green	–
275	Violet 14	Caledon Red Violet 2RN Indanthren Red Violet RRK	Violet	Brown–yellow	Blue–red	Yellow–red	–
280	–	Caledon Printing Scarlet FR	Violet	Red–yellow	Red	Green	–
285	Red 38	Indanthren Brilliant Pink BL	Violet	Yellow–red	Blue–red	Yellow–brown	–
290	–	Indanthren Brilliant Scarlet FGC	Black–violet	Yellow–red	Red	Black–green	–
			Blue				
295	Red 34	Indigosol Rubine IRB(F)	Blue	Violet	Yellow	Yellow–red	–
300	Red 13	Cibanone Red F6B Indanthren Rubine R Sandothrene Red F-N6B Tinon Red 6B-F	Green–blue	Black–blue–red	Yellow	Yellow–red	–
305	Red 43	Caledon Pink RL	Green–blue	Red–yellow	Yellow–red	Yellow–red	–
310	Red 34	Cibanone Red F3B Sandothrene Red F-N2B Tinon Red 2B-F	Green–blue	Red–violet	Green–yellow	Yellow–red	–

No.	Colour index	Dye	Alkaline hydrosulphite	Acid hydrosulphite	Nitric acid	Sulphuric acid	Acid permanganate
315	–	Indanthren Copper HGR	*Green* Green	Green	Red–yellow	Red–yellow	–
320	–	Indanthren Scarlet H4G	Green	Green	Yellow–red	Yellow–red	–
325	Red 14	Indanthren Scarlet GG Paradone Scarlet 2G	Yellow–green	Black–green	Yellow–red	Yellow–red	–
330	Red 15	Paradone Bordeaux RR Indanthren Bordeaux RR Indanthren Bordeaux HRR	Yellow–green	Brown–green	Red–yellow	Yellow–red	–
335	Red 46	Cibanone Brilliant Pink FG Sandothrene Brilliant Pink F-NG Tinon Brilliant Pink G-F	Blue–green	Red	Red	Red–brown	–
340	Red 19	Caledon Red X5B	Grey–blue–green	Yellow–red (stripped)	Blue–red	Yellow	–
345	Red 60	Cibanone Bordeaux F2G Sandothrene Bordeaux F–N2G Tinon Bordeaux 2G-F	Brown–green	Brown	Brown–red	Grey–green	–
350	Red 3	Indigosol Red AB Sandozol Red AB Tinosol Red AB	*Yellow* Yellow (stripped)	Yellow	Red	Blue–green	–

No.	Colour index	Dye	Alkaline hydrosulphite	Acid hydrosulphite	Nitric acid	Sulphuric acid	Acid permanganate
355	Red 6	Anthrasol Scarlet IB Ciba Scarlet F3B Cibantine Scarlet F3B Durindone Printing Scarlet R Indanthren Scarlet B Indanthren Scarlet BS Indigosol Scarlet IB(F) Sandothrene Scarlet F-3B Sandozol Scarlet F-2B Tina Scarlet 3B-F Tinosol Scarlet 3BL	Green–yellow	Red	Red	Green	–
360	Red 47	Indanthren Brilliant Rubine RB Indanthren Brilliant Rubine RBS Indanthren Printing Red 3B Sandothrene Pink BG Tina Pink BG	Green–yellow	Red	Blue–red	Green	–
365	Red 41	Ciba Pink B Durindone Red B Tetra Pink B Tina Pink B	Green–yellow	Grey–blue–red (stripped)	Blue–red	Green	–

No.	Colour index	Dye	Alkaline hydrosulphite	Acid hydrosulphite	Nitric acid	Sulphuric acid	Acid permanganate
370	Violet 2	Anthrasol Red Violet IRH Ciba Red F3BN Durindone Red 3B Indanthren Red Violet RH Indigosol Red Violet IRH Sandothrene Red F-3B Sandozol Red Violet F-RH Soledon Red 3B Tina Red 3B-F Tinosol Red Violet RH–F	Green–yellow	Grey–blue–red (stripped)	Blue–red	Green	–
375	Red 8	Indigosol Red I2B(F) Sandozol Red F-2B Tinosol Red 2B-F	Green–yellow	Red (stripped)	Red	Green	–
380	Red 1	Anthrasol Pink IR Ciba Brilliant Pink FR Cibantine Brilliant Pink FR Durindone Pink FF Indanthren Brilliant Pink R Indanthren Brilliant Pink RB Indanthren Brilliant Pink RP Indanthren Brilliant Pink RS Indigosol Pink IR(F)	Green–yellow	Red	Red	Red (on fibre), bleeds Green after a time	–

No.	Colour index	Dye	Alkaline hydrosulphite	Acid hydrosulphite	Nitric acid	Sulphuric acid	Acid permanganate
		Paradone Brilliant Pink R Sandothrene Brilliant Pink F-R Sandozol Pink F-R Soledon Pink FF Tina Brilliant Pink R-F Tinosol Pink RS-F					
385	–	Tetra Scarlet BGN	Green–yellow	Red (stripped)	Red	Black–brown	–
390	–	Ciba Brilliant Pink B Durindone Pink FB Indanthren Brilliant Pink B	Green–yellow	Red	Red	Red (on fibre), bleeds Green	–
395	–	Algol Scarlet RB Anthrasol Scarlet HB Ciba Scarlet BG Cibantine Scarlet 2B Durindone Scarlet 2B Indigosol Scarlet HB Sandozol Scarlet B Soledon Scarlet B Tetra Scarlet BG Tina Scarlet BG Tinosol Scarlet B	Green–yellow	Red (stripped)	Yellow–red	Violet (on fibre); bleeds Black–blue	–

No.	Colour index	Dye	Alkaline hydrosulphite	Acid hydrosulphite	Nitric acid	Sulphuric acid	Acid permanganate
400	–	Durindone Scarlet 3B Tetra Scarlet 2B Tina Scarlet 2B	Green–yellow	Red (stripped)	Yellow–red	Red–violet (on fibre); bleeds Black–green	–
405	Violet 3	Ciba Red F2B Durindone Magenta B Indanthren Magenta B Indanthren Magenta BR Indanthren Red Violet RRN Sandothrene Red F-2B Tina Red 2B-F	Green–yellow	Blue–red	Blue–red	Red–violet (on fibre); bleeds Green	–
410	Red 2	Anthrasol Brilliant Pink I3B Ciba Brilliant Pink F3B Indanthren Brilliant Pink 3B Indigosol Brilliant Pink I3B(F) Sandothrene Brilliant Pink F-3B Sandozol Brilliant Pink F-3B Tinosol Brilliant Pink 3B	Green–yellow	Blue–red	Red	Red	–
415	Red 36	Sandothrene Brilliant Pink 2B Tina Brilliant Pink 2B	Green–yellow	Blue–red	Red	Blue–red	–

No.	Colour index	Dye	Alkaline hydrosulphite	Acid hydrosulphite	Nitric acid	Sulphuric acid	Acid permanganate
420	–	Algol Scarlet GGN	Green–yellow	Red (stripped)	Yellow–red	Violet	–
425	Red 4	Ciba Bordeaux F2RN Indigosol Bordeaux I2RN Sandozol Bordeaux 2RN Tetra Bordeaux F-2RN Tina Bordeaux 2RN-F Tinosol Bordeaux 2RN	Green–yellow	Brown–red	Black–red	Blue–grey	–
430	Red 11	Durindone Printing Pink 2B Soledon Pink 2B	Green–yellow	Blue–red	Red	Green	–
435	Red 9	Sandozol Brilliant Pink 5B Tinosol Brilliant Pink 5B	Green–yellow	Red	Red	Red (on fibre); bleeds Green after a time	–
440	–	Durindone Scarlet 2GN	Green–yellow	Yellow–red (stripped)	Red	Violet	–
445	Red 28	Cibanone Red G Sandothrene Red NG Tinon Red G	Red–yellow	Red–yellow	Red–yellow	Yellow–red	–
450	Red 40	Indanthren Brilliant Scarlet RK Paradone Brilliant Scarlet RK	Red–yellow	Yellow–red	Green–yellow	Yellow–red	–

No.	Colour index	Dye	Alkaline hydrosulphite	Acid hydrosulphite	Nitric acid	Sulphuric acid	Acid permanganate
			Red				
455	Red 31	Caledon Brilliant Red 5B Indanthren Red F3B	Brown–red	Brown–yellow	Blue–red	Yellow	–
			Brown				
460	–	Indanthren Copper HR	Brown	Black–green	Red–yellow	Yellow–red	–
465	Red 25	Sandothrene Bordeaux N2B Tinon Bordeaux 2B	Red–brown	Brown	Black–red	Grey then Brown–green	–
			Black				
470	Red 51	Indanthren Red FRC	Black	Yellow–brown	Red	Red–brown	–
475	Violet 20	Caledon Rubine B	Black	Yellow–brown	Blue–red	Green	–
480	Red 42	Benzadone Red 5G	Blue–black	Yellow–red	Red–yellow	Red	–
485	–	Caledon Red 5G	Blue–black	Yellow–red	Red–yellow	Red	–
490	Red 18	Indanthren Bordeaux B	Green–black	Brown	Black–red	Grey–yellow	–
495	Red 44	Cibanone Brilliant Pink F2R Sandothrene Brilliant Pink F-N2R Tinon Brilliant Pink 2R-F	Green–black	Red	Red	Grey–red	–

No.	Colour index	Dye	Alkaline hydrosulphite	Acid hydrosulphite	Nitric acid	Sulphuric acid	Acid permanganate
500	Red 21	Caledon Red 4B Indanthren Rubine GR	Green–black	Brown	Red	Red	–
505	Red 54	Indanthren Brilliant Scarlet EFR	Green–black	Brown–red	Red	Brown–yellow	–
510	Red 24	Cibanone Red F4B Sandothrene Red F-N4B Tinon Red 4B-F	Red–black	Red–yellow	Red–yellow	Black–red	–
515	Red 20	Indanthren Rubine B	Brown–black	Brown–red	Black–red	Grey–yellow	–
520	–	Indanthren Brilliant Scarlet FR	Brown–black (Red–violet solution)	Red–yellow	Red	Black (on fibre), bleeds Yellow–green	–
525	Red 10	Anthrasol Red IFBB Benzadone Red FBB Caledon Brilliant Red 3B Caledon Printing Red 3B Cibanone Red FBB Cibantine Red FBB Indanthren Red FBB Indigosol Red IFBB(F) Paradone Brilliant Red FBB Paradone Brilliant Red 3BS	Brown–black	Red–yellow	Red	Grey–yellow (almost stripped)	–

No.	Colour index	Dye	Alkaline hydrosulphite	Acid hydrosulphite	Nitric acid	Sulphuric acid	Acid permanganate
		Sandothrene Red F-NF2B Sandozol Red F-FBB Soledon Red 2B Tinon Red F2B-F Tinosol Red F2B-F					
530	–	Indanthren Scarlet F3G	Brown–black (Red–violet solution)	Red–yellow	Red	Black (on fibre), bleeds Yellow–green	–

TABLE III. *Violet Dyes*

No.	Colour index	Dye	Alkaline hydrosulphite	Acid hydrosulphite	Nitric acid	Sulphuric acid	Acid permanganate
535	Violet 6	Indigosol Red Violet IRRL(F)	*Red–violet* Red–violet	Red–brown	Red–violet then Black–blue	Yellow–green	–
540	Violet 7	Indigosol Violet I5R(F)	Red–violet	Brown	Violet then Black–blue	Yellow–green	–
545	Violet 10	Benzadone Violet B Paradone Brilliant Violet B New	*Blue* Blue	Grey–blue	Blue then Grey–red–violet	Green	–
550	Violet 9	Benzadone Brilliant Violet 3B Caledon Brilliant Violet 3B Cibanone Violet F6B Indanthren Brilliant Violet 3B Indanthren Printing Violet F3B Paradone Brilliant Violet 3B Sandothrene Violet F-N3B Tinon Violet 6B-F	Blue	Blue–red	Violet	Green	–

No.	Colour index	Dye	Alkaline hydrosulphite	Acid hydrosulphite	Nitric acid	Sulphuric acid	Acid permanganate
555	Violet 1	Benzadone Brilliant Purple 2R Benzadone Brilliant Violet 2RBF Cibanone Violet F2RB Indanthren Brilliant Violet RR Paradone Brilliant Violet 2R Sandothrene Violet F-N2RB Tinon Violet 2RB-F	Green–blue	Red–violet	Red–violet	Green	–
560	Violet 1	(Similar brands) Anthrasol Brilliant Violet I4R Benzadone Brilliant Purple 4R Caledon Brilliant Purple 4R Cibanone Violet F4R Cibantine Brilliant Violet F4R Indanthren Brilliant Violet 4R Indanthren Printing VioletF4R Indigosol Brilliant Violet I4R(F) Paradone Brilliant Violet 4R Sandothrene Violet F-N4R Sandozol Brilliant Violet F-4R Soledon Brilliant Purple 2R Tinon Violet 4R-F Tinosol Brilliant Violet 4R-F	Green–blue	Red–violet	Red–violet	Green	–
565	–	Indigosol Brilliant Violet I2RB(F)	Green–blue	Red–violet	Red–violet	Green	–

No.	Colour index	Dye	Alkaline hydrosulphite	Acid hydrosulphite	Nitric acid	Sulphuric acid	Acid permanganate
570	Violet 11	Sandothrene Violet N2BW Tinon Violet 2BW	Green–blue	Violet	Violet	Green	–
575	Violet 13	Caledon Violet XBN Cibanone Violet FFB Indanthren Violet FFBN Tinon Violet FFBN	Grey–blue	Red–brown	Red–violet	Yellow–red	–
			Yellow				
580	Violet 8	Anthrasol Violet ARR Anthrasol Printing Violet IRR Indigosol Violet ARR Indigosol Printing Violet IRR	Yellow	Red–violet (stripped)	Red–violet	Green	–
585	–	Indanthren Printing Violet RF	Yellow	Red–grey (stripped)	Red–violet	Green	–
590	Violet 4	Ciba Violet F6R Indigosol Purple AR Indigosol Printing Purple IR Sandozol Printing Purple F-R Tetra Violet F-6R Tina Violet 6R-F Tinosol Printing Purple R-F	Red–yellow	Brown then Grey–green	Red–violet	Green	–

No.	Colour index	Dye	Alkaline hydrosulphite	Acid hydrosulphite	Nitric acid	Sulphuric acid	Acid permanganate
595	Violet 5	Anthrasol Violet ABBF Anthrasol Printing Violet IBBF Indanthren Printing Violet BBF Indigosol Violet ABBF Indigosol Printing Violet IBBF Sandozol Printing Violet F–BBF	Red–yellow	Blue–grey then Green–yellow	Violet	Blue–green	–
600	Violet 17	Caledon Brilliant Violet R Indanthren Brilliant Violet RK	*Red* Yellow–red	Red–violet	Red–violet	Green	–
605	Violet 15	Indanthren Brilliant Violet BBK	Yellow–red	Red–violet	Red–violet	Blue–green	–
610	Violet 12	Caledon Brilliant Violet 3R	Yellow–red	Red–violet	Red–violet	Green	–
615	Violet 21	Indanthren Brilliant Violet E5R	Brown–red	Red–violet	Red–violet	Green–blue	–
620	Violet 16	Indanthren Corinth RK	*Brown* Grey–brown	Brown	Black–red	Yellow–brown	–

TABLE IV. *Blue Dyes*

No.	Colour index	Dye	Alkaline hydrosulphite	Acid hydrosulphite	Nitric acid	Sulphuric acid	Acid permanganate
			Red–violet				
625	Blue 27	Cibanone Printing Blue F CBN Sandothrene Printing Blue F-NCBN	Red–violet	Yellow–brown	Blue	Brown	Blue
			Violet				
630	Blue 20	Benzadone Dark Blue BMS Benzadone Dark Blue BOA Benzadone Dark Blue BOR Caledon Dark Blue BM Cibanone Dark Blue FBOA Cibanone Dark Blue FMBA Indanthren Dark Blue BOA Paradone Dark Blue Paradone Dark Blue 58321 Sandothrene Dark Blue F-NBOA Sandothrene Dark Blue F-NMBA Tinon Dark Blue BO–F Tinon Dark Blue BOR Tinon Dark Blue MB-F	Violet	Brown–red	Red–black	Red–violet	Brown
635	Blue 31	Indanthren Blue CLG	Violet	Brown	Black–blue	Grey–yellow	Green–blue (largely stripped)

No.	Colour index	Dye	Alkaline hydrosulphite	Acid hydrosulphite	Nitric acid	Sulphuric acid	Acid permanganate
640	Blue 63	Indanthren Blue EB	Violet	Brown	Black–blue	Green	Brown (stripped)
645	Blue 64	Indanthren Blue ER	Violet	Brown	Violet	Green	Blue (stripped)
650	–	Indanthren Blue HCRK	Violet	Grey–brown	Blue	Yellow–brown	Blue
655	Blue 21	Indanthren Blue HCGK Indanthren Printing Blue HFG	Violet	Yellow–brown	Blue	Yellow–brown	Blue
660	Blue 30	Indanthren Blue CLB	Violet	Grey–blue	Blue	Yellow	Green–blue
665	Blue 52	Caledon Blue 3RC	Violet	Yellow–brown	Violet then Yellow–brown then Yellow slowly	Green	Grey–blue
670	Blue 17	Caledon Dark Blue 2R	Violet	Brown–red	Red–black	Red–violet	Yellow–brown
675	Blue 65	Indanthren Navy Blue ERT	Black–violet	Brown	Blue	Green	Blue–red (stripped)
			Blue				
680	Blue 16	Benzadone Dark Blue G Caledon Dark Blue G Caledon Printing Navy G Indanthren Navy Blue G Paradone Navy Blue G	Blue	Blue–red	Black–green	Blue–red	Brown

No.	Colour index	Dye	Alkaline hydrosulphite	Acid hydrosulphite	Nitric acid	Sulphuric acid	Acid permanganate
685	Blue 19	Indanthren Navy Blue BF	Blue	Red	Red–violet	Violet	Grey–green
690	–	Cibanone Navy Blue FGS	Blue	Violet	Green–black	Black–brown	–
695	Blue 12	Caledon Blue 3G					
		Indanthren Blue 3G					
		Indanthren Blue 3GN					
		Purified brands:-					
		Caledon Brilliant Blue 3G	Blue	Violet	Yellow	Green–brown	Green–yellow
		Caledon Printing Blue 3G					
		Indanthren Brilliant Blue 3G					
		Paradone Brilliant Blue 3G					
700	Blue 28	Indanthren Blue 3GF	Blue	Violet	Yellow	Green–brown	Yellow–green
705	Blue 4	Benzadone Blue RS					
		Caledon Blue XRN					
		Cibanone Blue FRS					
		Indanthren Blue RS					
		Indanthren Blue RSN					
		Indanthren Blue GP	Blue	Violet	Yellow	Green–brown	Yellow–green
		Indanthren Printing Blue KRS					
		Paradone Blue RS					
		Paradone Printing Blue FRS					
		Sandothrene Blue F-NRSN					
		Tinon Blue RS-F					
		Tinon Blue RSN–F					

No.	Colour index	Dye	Alkaline hydrosulphite	Acid hydrosulphite	Nitric acid	Sulphuric acid	Acid permanganate
		Purified brands:- Caledon Brilliant Blue RN Cibanone Brilliant Blue FR Indanthren Brilliant Blue R Paradone Brilliant Blue R					
710	Blue 14	Benzadone Blue GCD Caledon Blue GCP Cibanone Blue FGCD Indanthren Blue GCD Indanthren Blue GCDN Paradone Blue GCP Sandothrene Blue F–NGCD Sandothrene Blue F-NGCDN Tinon Blue GCP–F (Similar brand)	Blue	Violet	Yellow	Green–brown	Yellow–green
715	Blue 10	Caldeon Blue GXD Paradone Blue GCD Tinon Blue GCD (Similar brand)	Blue	Blue	Green then Yellow	Green–brown	Blue–green
720	Blue 6	Alizanthrene Blue RC Anthrasol Blue IBC Benzadone Blue RC Caledon Blue XRC Cibanone Blue FG Cibanone Blue FGF					

No.	Colour index	Dye	Alkaline hydrosulphite	Acid hydrosulphite	Nitric acid	Sulphuric acid	Acid permanganate
		Cibantine Blue FGF	Blue	Blue	Green then Yellow	Green–brown	Blue–green
		Indanthren Blue BC					
		Indanthren Blue BCS					
		Indigosol Blue IBC(F)					
		Paradone Blue RC					
		Sandothrene Blue NG					
		Sandozol Blue F-BC					
		Soledon Blue 2RC					
		Tinon Blue GF–F					
		Tinon Blue GL–F					
		Tinosol Blue BC–F					
		Indanthren Brilliant Blue RCL (Similar brand)					
725	–	Caledon Brilliant Blue 2RC	Blue	Violet	Grey–red	Yellow–green	Green–blue
730	–	Cibanone Blue F2R	Blue	Blue	Brown–grey	Grey–green	Green
735	Blue 7	Benzadone Blue 3G					
		Cibanone Blue F3G					
		Indanthren Blue Green FFB	Blue	Blue–red	Black–green	Brown–black	Yellow–green
		Indanthren Green Blue FFG					
		Paradone Blue Green FFB					
		Sandothrene Blue F-N3G					
		Tinon Blue 3G-F					
740	–	Benzadone Blue RLC	Blue	Violet	Brown	Green	Stripped

No.	Colour index	Dye	Alkaline hydrosulphite	Acid hydrosulphite	Nitric acid	Sulphuric acid	Acid permanganate
745	–	Indanthren Navy Blue RB	Blue	Violet	Blue	Black (on fibre) bleeds Violet	Grey–blue
750	Blue 26	Indanthren Cyanine B	Blue	Blue–red	Green, then Black	Blue–red	Yellow–red
755	Blue 62	Indanthren Blue HCBR	Blue	Violet	Green then Black–brown	Black (on fibre) bleeds Black–violet	Yellow–green
760	–	Caledon Printing Navy X	Blue	Red–violet	Violet	Violet	Violet
765	–	Indanthren Navy Blue TRG	Green–blue	Black–violet	Blue–black	Violet–black bleeds Violet	Black–blue
770	Blue 22	Indanthren Navy Blue TRR	Green–blue	Violet	Blue–black	Violet	Black–blue
775	Blue 18	Alizanthrene Navy Blue R Alizanthrene Navy Blue RT Benzadone Navy Blue R Caledon Navy Blue ART Caledon Navy Blue 2R Cibanone Navy Blue FRA Paradone Dark Blue RFW Sandothrene Dark Blue F-NR Tinon Navy Blue RA-F	Green–blue	Red–violet	Black–blue	Red–violet	Black–blue

No.	Colour index	Dye	Alkaline hydrosulphite	Acid hydrosulphite	Nitric acid	Sulphuric acid	Acid permanganate
780	Blue 25	Indanthren Navy Blue R Paradone Navy Blue R	Green–blue	Blue–red	Blue–green then Black–blue	Red–violet	Brown–green
785	–	Sandothrene Dark Blue N2R	Green–blue	Violet	Black–blue	Violet	Black–blue
790	Blue 67	Indanthren Blue HCBG	Green–blue	Violet	Green then Black–green	Brown–black	Yellow
795	–	Indanthren Printing Navy Blue RR	Green–blue	Black–blue–red	Blue–black then Black–red–violet	Black–violet	Black–blue
800	–	Indanthren Navy Blue TRFG	Green–blue *Green*	Blue	Blue–black	Brown	Blue
805	–	Sandothrene Printing Blue F-N2R	Blue–green	Red–violet	Violet	Violet	Violet
810	Blue 58	Indanthren Blue BP Indanthren Printing Blue BR	*Yellow* Yellow (stripped)	Blue	Violet	Green–blue	Stripped
815	Blue 1	Anthrasol O Indigo Indigo Ciba					

No.	Colour index	Dye	Alkaline hydrosulphite	Acid hydrosulphite	Nitric acid	Sulphuric acid	Acid permanganate
		Indigosol O Sandozol Blue O Soledon Indigo LL Tinosol Blue O	Green–yellow	Grey–blue (stripped)	Red–yellow	Blue–green	–
820	Blue 3	Indigo Ciba R Indigosol OR Sandozol Blue OR Tetra Blue R Tina Indigo R Tinosol Blue OR	Green–yellow	Grey–blue (stripped)	Red–yellow	Blue–green	–
825	Blue 34	Indigo 2R Indigo Ciba 2R Tina Indigo 2R	Green–yellow	Grey–blue (stripped)	Red–yellow	Blue–green	–
830	Blue 37	BASF Brilliant Indigo BB	Green–yellow	Grey–blue (stripped)	Violet (on fibre); bleeds Red–violet	Blue–green	–
835	Blue 40	Indanthren Printing Blue HR	Green–yellow	Violet	Black–violet	Blue–green	Violet
840	Blue 8	Anthrasol Blue AGG Anthrasol Printing Blue IGG Indanthren Printing Blue GG					

No.	Colour index	Dye	Alkaline hydrosulphite	Acid hydrosulphite	Nitric acid	Sulphuric acid	Acid permanganate
		Indigosol Blue AGG	Green–yellow	Blue (stripped)	Blue–green then Brown–yellow	Blue–green	–
		Indigosol Printing Blue IGG					
		Sandozol Printing Blue F-2G					
		Tinosol Printing Blue 2G–F					
845	Violet 19	Indanthren Printing Blue 3R	Green–yellow	Red–violet	Red–violet	Green–blue	Violet
850	Blue 41	BASF Brilliant Indigo B					
		BASF Brilliant Indigo BR	Red–yellow	Green–blue (stripped)	Black–blue then Brown then Red–yellow	Blue–green	–
		Ciba Blue BR					
		Tetra Blue BR					
		Tina Blue BR					
855	Blue 5	Anthrasol O4B					
		BASF Brilliant Indigo 4B					
		BASF Brilliant Indigo 4BC					
		Ciba Blue 2B					
		Cibantine Blue 2B					
		Durindone Blue 4BC	Red–yellow	Green–blue (stripped)	Black–blue then Brown then Red–yellow	Blue–green	–
		Indigosol O4B					
		Sandozol Blue O4B					
		Soledon Blue 4BC					
		Tetra Blue 2B					
		Tina Blue 2B					
		Tinosol Blue O4B					

No.	Colour index	Dye	Alkaline hydrosulphite	Acid hydrosulphite	Nitric acid	Sulphuric acid	Acid permanganate
860	–	Indigosol O6B	Red–yellow	Blue–green	Blue–green	Blue–green	–
865	Blue 2	Anthrasol O4G BASF Brilliant Indigo 4G	Red–yellow	Green–blue (stripped)	Green then Red–yellow	Blue–green	–
870	Blue 42	Hydron Blue G	Red–yellow	Yellow	Black–blue	Blue	Blue (largely stripped)
875	–	Hydron Blue B	Red–yellow	Yellow	Black–blue	Blue	Stripped
880	–	Hydron Blue GG	Red–yellow	Red–yellow	Blue	Black–blue	Blue (stripped)
885	Blue 43	Ciba Blue 2RH Hydron Blue R Hydron Blue 3R	Red–yellow	Yellow	Black–blue	Blue	Stripped
890	Blue 45	Ciba Blue RH	Red–yellow	Yellow	Black–blue	Blue	Blue (largely stripped)
895	Blue 44	Ciba Blue 3RH	Red–yellow	Yellow	Black–blue	Blue	Stripped

No.	Colour index	Dye	Alkaline hydrosulphite	Acid hydrosulphite	Nitric acid	Sulphuric acid	Acid permanganate
900	Blue 47	Hydron Blue RR Hydron Blue 3RN	Red–yellow	Yellow	Black–blue	Blue	Stripped
905	–	Benzindone Blue 2B	Red–yellow	Green–blue	Blue–grey	Black–blue (in fibre) bleeds Green–blue	Blue (stripped)
			Red				
910	Blue 33	Indanthren Turquoise Blue 3GK	Grey–blue–red	Green then Brown–green	Yellow–brown	Yellow–green then Brown–yellow	Red–grey
915	Blue 70	Cibanone Blue F4G Sandothrene Blue F-N4G	Black–blue–red	Yellow–brown	Red–violet	Black (on fibre) bleeds Violet	Blue–grey
			Grey				
920	–	Hydron Navy Blue CN	Yellow–grey	Yellow–red (stripped)	Black–blue	Blue	Blue (stripped)
			Black				
925	–	Indanthren Dark Blue DB	Blue–black	Brown–black	Brown–green	Black (on fibre) bleeds Violet	Brown–green
930	Blue 13	Indanthren Blue 5G	Blue–black	Black–red–violet	Green	Brown–green	Stripped
935	Blue 66	Indanthren Blue CLF	Green–black	Brown	Yellow–green	Yellow	Brown (stripped)

TABLE V. *Green Dyes*

No.	Colour index	Dye	Alkaline hydrosulphite	Acid hydrosulphite	Nitric acid	Sulphuric acid	Acid permanganate
			Violet				
940	–	Paradone Green G	Violet	Green	Brown–yellow	Brown–green	Yellow–green
945	–	Paradone Green 2G	Violet	Green	Black–green	Brown–green	Yellow–green
950	–	Indanthren Green G	Violet	Violet–black	Yellow–green	Brown–green	Green–yellow
955	–	Indanthren Green GG	Violet	Brown–green	Yellow–green	Brown–green	Green–yellow
			Blue				
960	Green 1	Anthrasol Green IB					
		Benzadone Jade Green B					
		Benzadone Jade Green XN					
		Benzadone Jade Green XBN					
		Caledon Jade Green XBN					
		Caledon Jade Green XN					
		Cibanone Brilliant Green FBF					
		Cibanone Brilliant Green F2B					
		Cibanone Brilliant GreenFBFF					
		Cibantine Brilliant Green FBF					
		Estersol Green IB					
		Indanthren Brilliant Green B	Blue	Blue–red	Grey–green then Yellow–brown	Blue–red	Brown
		Indanthren Brilliant Green FFB					
		Indigosol Green IB(F)					
		Paradone Jade Green B New					
		Paradone Jade Green BX New					

No.	Colour index	Dye	Alkaline hydrosulphite	Acid hydrosulphite	Nitric acid	Sulphuric acid	Acid permanganate
		Paradone Jade Green XS New Sandothrene Brilliant Green F-NBF Sandothrene Brilliant Green F-N2B Sandozol Green F-B Soledon Jade Green X Tinon Brilliant Green BF-F Tinon Brilliant Green 2BF Tinon Brilliant Green B2F-F Tinon Brilliant Green BFP Tinosol Green B-F					
965	Green 4	Caledon Jade Green 3B Indanthren Brilliant Green 3B Soledon Jade Green 3B	Blue	Blue–red	Grey–green then Yellow–brown	Blue–red	Red–brown
970	–	Caledon Jade Green G	Blue	Blue–red	Grey–green then Yellow–brown	Blue–red	Red–brown
975	Green 2	Anthrasol Green IGG Benzadone Jade Green 2G Caledon Jade Green 2G Cibanone Brilliant Green F2GF					

No.	Colour index	Dye	Alkaline hydrosulphite	Acid hydrosulphite	Nitric acid	Sulphuric acid	Acid permanganate
		Indanthren Brilliant Green GG Indanthren Brilliant Green 3GF Indigosol Green IGG(F) Paradone Jade Green 2G Sandothrene Brilliant Green F-N2GF Sandozol Green F-2G Soledon Jade Green 2G Tinon Brilliant Green 2GF-F Tinosol Green GG-F	Blue	Blue–red	Grey–green then Yellow–brown	Blue–red	Red–brown
980	–	Cibanone Brilliant Green F2G	Blue	Red	Grey–green then Brown–yellow	Red–brown	Yellow
985	–	Benzadone Jade Green 4G Caledon Jade Green 4G Indanthren Brilliant Green 4G Indanthren Brilliant Green 4GF Paradone Jade Green 4G	Blue	Blue–red	Grey–green then Brown–yellow	Red–brown	Yellow
990	–	Cibanone Brilliant Green F4G Sandothrene Brilliant Green F-N4G	Blue	Red	Grey–green then Brown–yellow	Red–brown	Green–yellow

No.	Colour index	Dye	Alkaline hydrosulphite	Acid hydrosulphite	Nitric acid	Sulphuric acid	Acid permanganate
995	–	Cibanone Brilliant Green F4GF Sandothrene Brilliant Green F-N4GF	Blue	Red	Grey–green then Brown–yellow	Red–brown	Yellow
1000	– –	Cibanone Brilliant Green F-5GF Sandothrene Brilliant Green F-N5GF	Blue	Red	Green then Brown–yellow (slowly)	Brown	Yellow
1005	–	Caledon Green G	Blue	Blue–red	Yellow–green then Brown	Red	Yellow–brown
1010	–	Caledon Green 2G	Blue	Blue–red	Yellow–green then Brown	Brown–red	Brown–yellow
1015	Green 9	Benzadone Green BN Caledon Green BN Cibanone Green 2B	Blue	Black–red	Black	Violet	Brown
1020	–	Benzadone Green 2B	Blue	Black–red	Black	Violet	Brown (largely stripped)
1025	–	Caledon Printing Jade Green 5G	Blue	Blue–red	Yellow–green then Brown–yellow	Brown–red	Yellow

No.	Colour index	Dye	Alkaline hydrosulphite	Acid hydrosulphite	Nitric acid	Sulphuric acid	Acid permanganate
1030	Blue 69	Indanthren Blue Green H4B	Blue	Violet	Green then Green–blue	Violet–brown (on fibre) bleeds Violet	Yellow
1035	Green 11	Caledon Green 2B Indanthren Green BB	Black–blue	Black–blue	Black–green	Blue–green	Brown (largely stripped)
1040	–	Indanthren Green GT	Black–blue	Brown–black	Green	Green	Brown–yellow
1045	Green 3	Anthrasol Olive Green IB Benzadone Olive Green B Caledon Olive Green B Cibanone Olive FB Cibantine Olive FB Indanthren Olive Green B Indigosol Olive Green IB(F) Paradone Olive Green B Sandothrene Olive F-N2B Sandozol Olive Green F-B Soledon Green G Tinon Olive B-F Tinon Olive BM Tinosol Olive Green B–F	Black–blue	Brown–black	Grey then Green	Green	Yellow

No.	Colour index	Dye	Alkaline hydrosulphite	Acid hydrosulphite	Nitric acid	Sulphuric acid	Acid permanganate
1050	Similar to Green 3	Cibanone Olive FBG Sandothrene Olive F-NBG Tinon Olive BG-F	Black–blue	Brown–black	Black–brown (on fibre) does not return to Green bleeds Black–brown	Green	Brown–yellow
1055	Green 5	Indanthren Olive Green GG	Black–blue	Brown–black	Black–green (on fibre) then Red–brown bleeds Red–brown	Green	Yellow–brown
1060	Green 30	Anthrasol Olive Green IBB Cibanone Olive F2B Cibantive Olive F2B Sandothrene Olive F-NF2B Tinon Olive 2B-F Tinosol Olive Green 2B-F	Black–blue	Brown–black	Yellow–brown	Green	Yellow
1065	–	Indigosol Olive Green IBU(F)	Black–blue	Black	Black–brown	Green	Brown–yellow

No.	Colour index	Dye	Alkaline hydrosulphite	Acid hydrosulphite	Nitric acid	Sulphuric acid	Acid permanganate
1070	Green 41	Indanthren Olive HG	Black–blue	Black–brown	Brown	Green	Yellow
1075	Green 14	Indanthren Olive GG Indanthren Printing Olive GW	*Green* Green	Grey–green	Green–black	Green–brown	Yellow (largely stripped)
1080	Green 7	Caledon Olive GL Cibanone Olive F2G Tetra Olive F-N2G Tinon Olive 2G-F Cibanone Khaki FGR Tetra Olive F-NGR Tinon Khaki GR (Similar brands)	Blue–green	Brown–green	Black	Brown–green	Yellow (largely stripped)
1085	Green 12	Indanthren Green 4G	Grey–green	Green–brown	Yellow–brown	Red–yellow	Stripped
1090	Green 13 Green 13	Caledon Olive MW Indanthren Olive MW	Black–green	Green	Green then Brown–green slowly	Green–black	Yellow
1095	Green 26	Caledon Olive OMW	Black–green	Black	Green then Brown–green slowly	Green–black	Yellow

No.	Colour index	Dye	Alkaline hydrosulphide	Acid hydrosulphite	Nitric acid	Sulphuric acid	Acid permanganate
1100	Green 27	Caledon Olive RMW	Black–green	Black	Green	Green–black	Yellow
1105	Green 40	Indanthren Olive RMW	Black–green	Black	Green	Green–black	Yellow
1110	Green 29	Cibanone Olive FB2G Sandothrene Olive F-NB2G Tinon Olive B2G–F	Black–green	Black–green	Black–green	Green–black	Brown–yellow
1115	Green 35	Indanthren Olive Green EBG	Black–green	Black–green	Grey–green	Green–blue	Yellow–brown
1120	Green 24	Indanthren Brilliant Green H3G	*Yellow* Yellow	Yellow–green	Green	Black	Green (stripped)
1125	Green 21	Anthrasol Green I3G	Yellow	Brown–yellow	Green	Grey–brown	Stripped
1130	–	Indanthren Khaki DNE	*Brown* Brown	Yellow–brown	Brown–green	Black–brown	Green–brown
1135	–	Indanthren Khaki HS	Brown	Grey–green	Brown–green	Brown–black	Green–brown
1140	Green 16	Caledon Green 7G	Violet–brown	Red–brown	Green	Yellow–brown	Yellow–green (largely stripped)

No.	Colour index	Dye	Alkaline hydrosulphite	Acid hydrosulphite	Nitric acid	Sulphuric acid	Acid permanganate
1145	Green 32	Indanthren Khaki E3G	Green–brown	Grey–green	Black–green	Brown–black	Yellow
1150	Green 17	Indanthren Olive 3G	Yellow–brown	Brown–yellow	Grey–green	Yellow–brown	Brown–green
1155	Green 33	Indanthren Olive GRL	Yellow–brown	Grey–green	Grey	Red–violet	Green–grey
1160	Black 27	Benzadone Olive R Caledon Olive R Cibanone Olive F2R Indanthren Olive R Paradone Olive R Sandothrene Olive F-N2R Tinon Olive 2R-F	Red–brown	Yellow–brown	Green–black	Black–red	Brown–green
1165	Green 8	Caledon Khaki 2G Cibanone Khaki F2G Indanthren Khaki GG Sandothrene Khaki F-N2G Tinon Khaki GG-F	Red–brown	Yellow–green	Brown–green	Black–blue	Brown–green
1170	Brown 47	Caledon Khaki R	Red–brown	Yellow	Grey–yellow	Blue–black	Brown
1175	–	Indanthren Olive GR	Black–brown	Brown–green	Green–black	Black	Brown–green

No.	Colour index	Dye	Alkaline hydrosulphite	Acid hydrosulphite	Nitric acid	Sulphuric acid	Acid permanganate
1180	–	Indanthren Olive EG	Black–brown	Green	Green–black	Black (on fibr bleeds Black–blue	Brown–green
1185	–	Indanthren Olive EGR	Black–brown	Black–green	Black–green	Black	Brown–green
1190	–	Indanthren Olive 4G	Black–brown	Brown	Green–brown	Red–black	Green
1195	Green 31	Indanthren Yellow Green GC	*Black* Violet–grey	Brown	Red	Red–violet	Yellow (stripped)
1200	Green 6	Caledon Green RC	Blue–grey	Violet–black	Green–brown	Blue–green	Stripped
1205	Black 25	Anthrasol Grey IT Benzadone Olive T Caledon Olive D Cibanone Olive FS Indanthren Olive T Indigosol Grey ISG(F) Paradone Olive T Sandothrene Olive F-NT Sandozol Grey F-SG Soledon Olive D Tinon Olive S-F	Black	Yellow–brown	Black–green (on fibre) bleeds Red–violet	Green	Brown–yellow

No.	Colour index	Dye	Alkaline hydrosulphite	Acid hydrosulphite	Nitric acid	Sulphuric acid	Acid permanganate
1210	Green 28	Cibanone Green F-6G Sandothrene Green F-N6G Tinon Green 6G-F	Red–black	Grey–green	Brown–green	Yellow–brown	Green
1215	–	Indanthren Green 6GC	Red–black	Red–brown	Green	Yellow–brown	Green–yellow

TABLE VI. *Brown Dyes*

No.	Colour index	Dye	Alkaline hydrosulphite	Acid hydrosulphite	Nitric acid	Sulphuric acid	Acid permanganate
1220	–	Indanthren Black Brown R	*Blue–red or Red–violet* Blue–red	Red–brown	Green–brown (on fibre); bleeds Red–yellow	Black–blue–red	–
1225	Brown 70	Indanthren Red Brown GGR	Blue–red	Brown–yellow	Yellow–brown	Blue	–
1230	Brown 31	Indanthren Red Brown R	Red–violet *Violet*	Red–brown	Red–brown	Brown–green	–
1235	Brown 41	Indanthren Maroon BR	Black–violet	Red–brown	Black–red–brown	Blue–black	–
1240	Brown 56	Indanthren Black–Brown RV	Black–violet	Black–brown	Black	Black–green	–
1245	Brown 50	Indanthren Brown GCW	Black–violet	Yellow–brown	Brown	Green–blue	–
1250	–	Caledon Printing Brown 01385	*Blue* Blue	Black–brown	Yellow–brown	Brown	–
1255	Brown 22	Indanthren Printing Brown 5R	*Green* Green	Green	Yellow–red	Yellow–red	–
1260	Brown 58	Indanthren Red Brown HBR	Green	Green	Brown–red	Brown–red	–

No.	Colour index	Dye	Alkaline hydrosulphite	Acid hydrosulphite	Nitric acid	Sulphuric acid	Acid permanganate
1265	Brown 57	Indanthren Printing Brown HRR Cibanone Printing Brown F2R	Green	Black–green	Brown–red	Brown–red	–
1270	Brown 14	Indanthren Printing Brown B	Brown–green	Green	Black–red	Black–red	–
1275	Brown 33	Cibanone Brown F2BR Sandothrene Brown F-N2BR Tinon Brown 2BR-F	Black–green	Brown–green	Brown	Black (on fibre) bleeds Green	–
			Yellow				
1280	Brown 5	Anthrasol Brown IRRD Benzindone Brown G Ciba Brown FG Durindone Brown G Indanthren Brown RRD Indigosol Brown IRRD(F) Sandothrene Brown F-G Sandozol Brown F-RRD Tina Brown G-F Tinosol Brown 2RD-F	Yellow	Brown (stripped)	Yellow–brown	Blue	–
1285	Brown 48	Ciba Brown F2B Tina Brown 2B-F	Yellow	Yellow–brown	Yellow–brown	Violet	–

No.	Colour index	Dye	Alkaline hydrosulphite	Acid hydrosulphite	Nitric acid	Sulphuric acid	Acid permanganate
1290	Brown 42	Indanthren Printing Brown R	Yellow	Red–yellow	Red–brown	Yellow–brown	–
1295	Brown 1	Anthrasol Brown IBR Benzadone Brown BR Caledon Dark Brown 3R Cibanone Brown FBR Cibantine Brown FBR Indanthren Brown BR Indigosol Brown IBR(F) Paradone Red Brown 2RD Sandothrene Brown F–NBR Sandozol Brown F–BR Soledon Dark Brown 3R Tinon Brown BR–F Tinosol Brown BR–F	Yellow	Brown–green	Red–brown	Green–black	–
1300	–	Ciba Brown FV Tina Brown VD	Yellow	Red–brown	Brown	Blue	–
1305	–	Indanthren Printing Brown BT	Red–yellow *Red*	Green–brown	Brown	Brown	–
1310	Brown 8	Indanthren Red Brown GR	Red	Green–brown	Brown–red	Red–black	–
1315	–	Benzadone Brown 2G Caledon Brown 2GN Cibanone Brown F2G	Brown–red	Yellow–brown	Brown	Black (on fibre) bleeds Black–blue	–

No.	Colour index	Dye	Alkaline hydrosulphite	Acid hydrosulphite	Nitric acid	Sulphuric acid	Acid permanganate
		Indanthren Brown GG Paradone Brown 2G					
1320	–	Cibanone Brown RN	Brown–red	Yellow–brown	Red–brown	Black (on fibre) bleeds Black–blue	–
1325	Brown 3	Benzadone Brown R Caledon Brown R Cibanone Brown FGR Indanthren Brown R Paradone Brown R Sandothrene Brown F-NR Soledon Brown R Tinon Brown GR-F Purified brand:- Indanthren Brown FFR	Brown–red	Yellow–brown	Brown–red	Black (on fibre) bleeds Black–blue	–
1330	Brown 25	Indanthren Red Brown 5RF	Brown–red	Yellow–brown	Brown–red	Violet	–
1335	Brown 49	Caledon Dark Brown 2G	Brown–red	Yellow–brown	Brown	Red–brown	–
1340	Brown 35	Cibanone Yellow Brown FG					
		Sandothrene Yellow Brown F-NG Tinon Yellow Brown G-F	Brown–red	Yellow–brown	Brown–green	Black–green (on fibre) bleeds Green–blue	–

No.	Colour index	Dye	Alfialine hydrosulphite	Acid hydrosulphite	Nitric acid	Sulphuric acid	Acid permanganate
1345	Brown 36	Sandothrene Red Brown F-NR Tinon Red Brown R-F	Brown–red	Red–brown	Brown–green	Black (on fibre) bleeds Blue–black	–
1350	–	Benzadone Brown GB	Brown–red	Yellow–brown	Brown	Black–brown	–
1355	–	Indanthren Printing Brown HTM	Black–red	Black–brown	Yellow–brown	Black–red (on fibre) bleeds Red–violet	
1360	Brown 38	Caledon Dark Brown 6R	*Brown* Brown	Brown–yellow	Red–brown	Blue	–
1365	Brown 45	Indanthren Red Brown RR	Brown	Brown–yellow	Red–brown	Blue	–
1370	–	Caledon Dark Brown AN	Brown	Yellow–brown	Yellow–brown	Black (on fibre) bleeds Black–blue	–
1375	–	Caledon Brown G Cibanone Brown FBG Indanthren Brown G Sandothrene Brown F-NBG Tinon Brown BG-F	Brown	Yellow–brown	Yellow–brown	Black–red (on fibre) bleeds Red–violet	–

No.	Colour Index	Dye	Alkaline hydrosulphite	Acid hydrosulphite	Nitric acid	Sulphuric acid	Acid permanganate
1380	–	Cibanone Brown FG Sandothrene Brown F-NG	Brown	Yellow–brown	Brown	Black–red (on fibre) bleeds Red–violet	–
1385	–	Indanthren Brown LG	Brown	Brown	Brown	Green–blue	–
1390	Brown 32	Cibanone Brown FRV Indigosol Brown IRV(F) Sandothrene Brown F-NRV Sandozol Brown F-RV Tinon Brown RV-F Tinosol Brown RV–F	Brown	Yellow–brown	Red–brown	Green–brown	–
1395	–	Indanthren Red Brown 3RB	Brown	Yellow–brown	Red–brown	Black–brown	–
1400	Brown 27	Paradone Red Brown 5RD	Brown	Green–brown	Brown	Brown–green	–
1405	Brown 55	Indanthren Brown LMG	Brown	Brown	Brown	Green–blue	–
1410	–	Indanthren Printing Brown RL	Brown	Brown	Brown–red	Black–violet	–
1415	Brown 19	Indanthren Bronze GC	Brown	Brown	Brown	Violet–black then Brown–black	–
1420	Brown 4	Indanthren Red Brown GD	Brown	Brown	Red–brown	Black–brown	

No.	Colour index	Dye	Alkaline hydrosulphite	Acid hydrosulphite	Nitric acid	Sulphuric acid	Acid permanganate
1425	–	Sandothrene Brown F-V	Brown	Brown	Brown	Blue	–
1430	Brown 26	Indanthren Brown 3GT	Green–brown	Green–brown	Green–brown	Green–blue	–
1435	Brown 44	Indanthren Brown GR	Yellow–brown	Brown–green	Brown	Yellow–brown	–
1440	Brown 6	Cibanone Brown F3B Cibantine Brown F3B Indigosol Brown I3B(F) Sandothrene Brown F-N3B Sandozol Brown F-3B Tinon Brown 3B-F Tinosol Brown 3B-F	Yellow–brown	Brown	Brown	Black (on fibre) bleeds Violet	–
1445	Brown 65	Cibanone Printing Brown F3R	Yellow–brown	Red–brown	Red–brown	Black (on fibre) bleeds Violet	–
1450	Brown 9	Indanthren Brown NG Indanthren Brown NGS	Red–brown	Brown	Brown	Blue	–
1455	Orange 14	Caledon Orange Brown 2G	Red–brown	Brown	Red–yellow	Red–yellow then Green	–
1460	Brown 30	Caledon Brown 3G	Red–brown	Yellow–brown	Brown	Green	–
1465	–	Paradone Printing Brown TM	Red–brown	Yellow–brown	Yellow–brown	Blue–red	–

No.	Colour index	Dye	Alkaline hydrosulphite	Acid hydrosulphite	Nitric acid	Sulphuric acid	Acid permanganate
1470	–	Paradone Printing Brown TMI	Red–brown	Yellow–brown	Yellow–brown	Blue–red	–
1475	–	Ciba Brown FCH	Red–brown	Red–brown	Brown	Blue	–
1480	Brown 11	Cibanone Red Brown RRF Tinon Red Brown 2RF	Yellow–brown	Brown–green	Red–brown	Black	–
1485	Brown 17	Indanthren Black Brown NT Indanthren Black Brown NTS	Red–brown	Red–brown	Brown	Black–violet	–
1490	Brown 28	Caledon Printing Brown 4R	Black–brown	Brown	Yellow–brown	Violet	–
1495	Brown 23	Caledon Brown B	*Black* Black	Grey–brown	Brown–grey	Black–brown	–

TABLE VII. *Grey and Black Dyes*

No.	Colour index	Dye	Alkaline hydrosulphite	Acid hydrosulphite	Nitric acid	Sulphuric acid	Acid permanganate
1500	–	Benzadone Direct Black R	*Red–violet* Red–violet	Red–brown	Black	Black (on fibre), bleeds Violet	Yellow–brown
1505	–	Benzadone Direct Black 2G	*Violet* Violet	Red–brown	Black	Black (on fibre), bleeds Red–violet	Yellow–brown
1510	–	Caledon Direct Black BN	Violet	Black–brown	Black	Black–violet	Yellow–brown
1515	Black 9	Anthra Grey BT Benzadone Direct Black RB Cibanone Black FDRB Indanthren Direct Black RB Indanthren Direct Black RBS Sandothrene Black F-NDRB Tinon Direct Black DRB-F	Violet	Black–red	Black	Black (on fibre), bleeds Red–violet	Yellow–brown
1520	–	Indanthren Direct Black B	Violet	Red–brown	Black	Black (on fibre), bleeds Black–blue	Yellow–brown
1525	–	Paradone Direct Black RS New	Violet	Red–brown	Black	Black (on fibre), bleeds Blue–red	Yellow–brown

No.	Colour index	Dye	Alkaline hydrosulphite	Acid hydrosulphite	Nitric acid	Sulphuric acid	Acid permanganate
1530	–	Paradone Direct Black BG	Violet	Red–brown	Black	Black (on fibre), bleeds Blue–red	Yellow–brown
1535	Black 10	Sandothrene Black F-N2G Tinon Direct Black 2G-F	Violet	Black–red	Black	Black (on fibre), bleeds Brown–black	Black–green
1540	–	Cibanone Black FBA	Violet	Black–red	Black	Black (on fibre), bleeds Black–blue	Brown
1545	–	Indanthren Direct Black R	Violet	Red–brown	Black	Black (on fibre), bleeds Black–blue	Brown–yellow
1550	–	Cibanone Black FBAN	Violet	Red–brown	Black	Black (on fibre), bleeds Blue	Yellow brown
1555	–	Cibanone Black FR Sandothrene Black F-NR	Violet	Black	Black	Black (on fibre), bleeds Violet	Brown–yellow
1560	–	Caledon Grey AC Tinon Grey AC	Violet	Brown–red	Grey–brown	Red–violet	Red–brown

No.	Colour index	Dye	Alkaline hydrosulphite	Acid hydrosulphite	Nitric acid	Sulphuric acid	Acid permanganate
1565	Black 31	Indanthren Grey CL	Violet	Brown	Grey	Yellow	Red–brown
1570	–	Caledon Grey 2RC	Grey–violet	Yellow–brown	Black–violet then Brown	Black	Grey–brown
			Blue				
1575	–	Indanthren Grey RRH	Blue	Black–brown	Brown–yellow	Green–black	Grey–red–brown
1580	Black 16	Benzadone Grey 3B Caledon Grey 3B Indanthren Grey 3B Paradone Grey 3B	Blue	Brown–red	Blue–black	Red–violet	Brown–yellow
1585	Black 23	Paradone Grey B Paradone Grey R (Similar brand)	Blue	Grey–red	Grey–brown	Black–red (on fibre), bleeds Red–violet	Brown–yellow (largely stripped)
1590	Green 9	Benzadone Black NB Caledon Black 2BM Caledon Black NB Cibanone Black F2B Indanthren Black BB Paradone Black AB New Sandothrene Black F-N2B Tinon Black 2B-F	Blue	Black–red	Black	Black (on fibre), bleeds Red–violet	Brown

No.	Colour index	Dye	Alkaline hydrosulphite	Acid hydrosulphite	Nitric acid	Sulphuric acid	Acid permanganate
1595	Black 7	Cibanone Black F2BA Cibanone Black F3BA Sandothrene Black F-N2BA Sandothrene Black F-N3BA Tinon Black 3BA–F	Blue	Black–red	Black	Black (on fibre), bleeds Violet	Green–brown
1600	–	Tinon Black CAC	Blue	Black–red	Black	Black (on fibre), bleeds Red–violet	Yellow–brown
1605	Black 34	Caledon Direct Black AC Caledon Direct Black G Caledon Direct Black R	Red	Black–red	Black	Black (on fibre), bleeds Red–violet	Yellow–brown
1610	–	Caledon Printing Black R	Blue	Black–red	Brown–black	Black	Black
1615	–	Indanthren Printing Black BR	Blue	Black–red	Black	Black (on fibre), bleeds Violet	Yellow–brown
1620	Black 39	Cibanone Printing Black F2B Sandothrene Printing Black F-N2B	Blue	Blue–red	Grey	Black (on fibre), bleeds Violet	Red–brown

No.	Colour index	Dye	Alkaline hydrosulphite	Acid hydrosulphite	Nitric acid	Sulphuric acid	Acid permanganate
1625	–	Cibanone Printing Black FN	Blue	Red–black	Brown–black	Black–blue (on fibre), bleeds Violet	Brown
1630	Black 61	Indigosol Printing Black BZ	Blue	Blue–red	Brown–black	Black (on fibre), bleeds Black–green	Yellow–brown
1635	Black 20	Indanthren Grey GG	Blue	Brown–red	Black (on fibre) bleeds Green–blue	Violet	Brown–yellow
1640	–	Caledon Printing Black 2R	Green–blue	Black–red	Brown–black	Black (on fibre), bleeds Red–violet	Green–brown
			Green				
1645	Black 30	Cibanone Grey F2GR Sandothrene Grey F-N2GR Tinon Grey 2GR-F	Green	Red–black	Blue–black	Green	Red–brown
1650	–	Ciba Printing Black BDN	Yellow–green	Black–blue–red	Brown–black	Blue	Brown–black

No.	Colour index	Dye	Alkaline hydrosulphite	Acid hydrosulphite	Nitric acid	Sulphuric acid	Acid permanganate
1655	–	Ciba Printing Black FTL Durindone Printing Black TL Indanthren Printing Black TL Sandothrene Printing Black TL Tina Printing Black TL-F	Yellow–green	Black–green	Black (on fibre) bleeds Red–yellow	Black (on fibre), bleeds Green–black	Black
1660	Black 35	Indanthren Printing Black BGL	Yellow–green	Black	Black	Black (on fibre), bleeds Blue–black	Black
1665	–	Ciba Printing Deep Black BD	Yellow–green	Black–green	Yellow–brown (on fibre), bleeds Red–yellow	Black (on fibre), bleeds Green–black then Red	Brown
1670	–	Benzadone Grey R	Blue–green	Grey–red–violet	Blue–grey	Grey–red–brown	Blue–grey
1675	Black 8	Benzadone Grey M Caledon Grey M Indanthren Grey M Paradone Grey M	Blue–green	Black–red	Green–black then Green–blue	Green	Green–yellow
1680	Black 8	Purified brand:– Indanthren Grey MG	Blue–green	Black–red	Green–black then Violet	Green	Green–yellow

No.	Colour index	Dye	Alkaline hydrosulphite	Acid hydrosulphite	Nitric acid	Sulphuric acid	Acid permanganate
		Paradone Grey MG					
1685	–	Benzadone Grey G	Brown–green	Grey–red	Grey	Grey–red–brown	Grey
1690	–	Benzadone Grey B	Grey–green	Grey–brown	Green–grey	Grey–red–brown	Grey
1695	–	Durindone Printing Black G	Black–green	Blue–black	Yellow–brown	Black (on fibre), bleeds Violet	Yellow–brown
			Yellow				
1700	–	Cibantine Printing Black BM	Yellow	Green	Grey–violet	Blue–black	Grey
1705	–	Sandozol Printing Black R	Yellow	Green	Grey–violet	Blue–black	Grey
1710	–	Indigosol Printing Black AB2N	Yellow	Green	Grey–violet	Black (on) fibre), bleeds Brown–red	Blue–grey
1715	Black 2	Anthrasol Printing Black IB Indanthren Printing Black B	Green–yellow	Grey (stripped)	Black	Black (on fibre), bleeds Black–blue	Brown (largely stripped)
1720	Black 1	Anthrasol Grey IBL Ciba Printing Black FBL					

No.	Colour index	Dye	Alkaline hydrosulphite	Acid hydrosulphite	Nitric acid	Sulphuric acid	Acid permanganate
		Cibantine Grey FBL	Red–yellow	Black–green (stripped)	Black	Black (on fibre), bleeds Blue–green	Black
		Durindone Printing Black BL Estersol Grey IBL Indanthren Printing Black BL Indigosol Grey IBL(F) Sandozol Grey F-BL Soledon Grey B Tetra Printing Black F-BL Tina Grey BL Tina Printing Black BL-F Tinosol Grey BL-F					
1725			Red–yellow	Black–green (stripped)	Black	Black (on fibre), bleeds Blue–green	Black
	–	Tetra Grey BL					
1730			Red–yellow	Yellow–green	Brown–red	Black (on) fibre), bleeds Green	Violet
	–	Durindone Black BNP					
1735			Red–yellow	Green–yellow	Violet–brown	Grey–blue	Blue–grey (largely stripped)
	–	Indanthren Printing Grey HGL					
1740			Brown–yellow	Grey–green–brown	Brown	Black (on fibre), bleeds Green–blue	Black–violet
	–	Durindone Printing Black AN					

No.	Colour index	Dye	Alkaline hydrosulphite	Acid hydrosulphite	Nitric acid	Sulphuric acid	Acid permanganate
1745	Black 6	Anthrasol Blue Black IRD	Brown–yellow	Grey–green	Black–violet	Black (on fibre), bleeds Black–green	Blue–grey (stripped)
			Brown				
1750	Black 33	Cibanone Grey F3G Sandothrene Grey F-N3G Tinon Grey 3G-F	Brown	Grey–green–yellow	Black	Green–black	Grey
1755	Black 5	Cibantine Grey F3G Indigosol Grey I3F(F) Sandozol Grey F-3F Tinosol Grey 3F-F	Brown	Grey–green–yellow	Brown–black	Brown–black	Grey
1760	Black 4	Anthrasol Printing Black IGR	Yellow–brown	Green–brown	Black–red	Blue–black	Brown–green
1765	Black 32	Indanthren Grey HBR	Violet–brown	Brown	Black–brown	Black	Stripped
1770	–	Indanthren Grey EBN	Black–brown	Brown	Blue–grey	Black–brown	Grey–green
			Black				
1775	Black 44	Indanthren Grey EGR	Grey	Grey–brown	Grey	Grey–green	Yellow (stripped)
1780	Black 19	Indanthren Grey NC	Grey	Black	Black–green	Green	Yellow–brown

No.	Colour index	Dye	Alkaline hydrosulphite	Acid hydrosulphite	Nitric acid	Sulphuric acid	Acid permanganate
1785	Black 29	Cibanone Grey FBG Indanthren Grey BG Sandothrene Grey F-NBG Tinon Grey BG-F	Red–grey	Brown	Red–black	Yellow–green	Violet–brown
1790	–	Cibanone Grey F2BR	Black	Blue–grey	Grey–green then Grey–violet	Green	Brown–yellow
1795	–	Indanthren Printing Black HC	Green–black	Black	Black (on fibre) bleeds Red–brown	Black (on fibre), bleeds Red–brown	Black–brown
1800	Black 24	Caledon Printing Grey B	Blue–black	Violet	Blue–black	Red–violet	Brown

Chapter 4 IDENTIFICATION OF THE CLASSES OF DYES COMMONLY FOUND ON CELLULOSIC MATERIALS

A FEW simple tests are described below which have been found reliable in distinguishing the various types of dyes commonly found on cellulosic materials. It is necessary that the tests should be carried out in the order given.

TEST 1

A small sample of the dyed material is cut into small pieces and placed in a test tube. One ml of 75 per cent sulphuric acid is added and the tube is immersed in a water bath at 60°C for 5 min. It is shaken at intervals until a clear solution is obtained. Two ml of water are added and the contents of the tube are filtered through a 5·5 cm Whatman's No. 1 filter paper.

Reactive dyes give a coloured filtrate and little or no staining on the filter paper, whereas all other cellulosic dyes are retained on the filter paper giving a virtually colourless filtrate. Some reactive dyes stain the paper and some *direct* dyes may give a coloured filtrate, but it is usually possible to distinguish between the two classes by examination of the stain. Staining from reactive dyes is spread evenly over the paper and can be partially washed out with hot distilled water. Staining from other dyes is in the form of discrete particles and the class of dye often may be identified by washing the filter paper with various solutions. Hot distilled water deepens the stain caused by direct dyes. Vat and sulphur dyes may be identified by washing with hot alkaline hydrosulphite solution. This test may be used in conjunction with those recommended by I.C.I. Ltd.[1] and with the procedure described by F. Jordinson and R. Lockwood.[2,3]

TEST 2

A small sample of the dyed material is wrapped up in a piece of carefully bleached linen or cotton cloth (about 1 in. square), and tightly bound in the form of a roll with white sewing thread. The roll is placed in boiling distilled water, and boiled for 5 min. The roll is then opened out and the linen examined. *Direct* dyes bleed on to and dye the linen. Direct dyeings after-treated with products such as Fixanol (I.C.I.), or developed by diazotizing and coupling to improve their fastness to water and washing, stain the bleached material in this test, although not as heavily as the dyeing without after-treatment. The presence of direct dyes can sometimes be confirmed by placing a small sample of the dyeing in concentrated hydrochloric acid. Some direct dyes give distinct colour changes, e.g. C.I. Direct Yellow 12 becomes violet. Some reactive dyes also show a colour change in concentrated hydrochloric acid.

TEST 3

A small sample of the dyed material is wrapped up as in Test 2 and boiled for a few seconds in alkaline hydrosulphite solution (the reagent used in Test I, p. 4). After allowing to stand for 5 min in the hot liquor, the roll is opened and the linen examined. *Vat* and *sulphur* dyes are "vatted" and mark-off on to the linen. Immediately on opening the roll both the dyed material and the stain on the linen will be the colour of the alkaline "vat" and both will oxidize back to the dye on exposure to air. [N.B. *Alizarin blue* behaves like a vat dye in this test, but an additional test for its presence is given under Test 6 below.] *Insoluble azo* dyes, derived from brenthols or naphthols are unaffected by this treatment, or if of comparatively low resistance to reduction, they may be reduced to green–yellow or brown decomposition products. In the latter case there may bc a stain on the linen, but this will not re-oxidize in the air to the original colour. In this test *Primuline red* (primuline diazotized and developed with β-naphthol) gives a yellow stain on the linen, as may be obtained from azoic reds. *Primuline red* is, however, distinguished by rinsing the stained linen and treating for 5 min in a solution containing 1 per cent sodium nitrite and a few drops of hydrochloric acid, and then in a solution made by dissolving a few crystals of β-naphthol in 2 per cent caustic soda solution, when the red colour is redeveloped. *Direct* dyes generally are destroyed with the formation of practically colourless decomposition products. Exceptions to this general rule are (a) the thiazole type of yellow direct dyes, e.g. Primuline, which is unaffected by reduction and remains yellow, giving a yellow stain in the bleached material; (b) certain types of direct dyes, which give coloured decomposition products, e.g. the dyed shade may change to red, red–violet, or blue, and a stain of the same colour as the decomposition products is left on the bleached material, but the original dyed shade is not reproduced on air oxidation. These exceptions to the general behaviour of direct dyeings in the test should not lead to difficulties provided that Test 1 above is always carried out first. With dyeings of *Turkey red*, although the dyed material itself is little affected and remains red in the above test, a yellow–brown stain is obtained on the linen which re-oxidizes in the air to red. *Turkey red* should be confirmed by the following test. A small sample of the dyed material is boiled in dilute hydrochloric acid (1 part concentrated acid and 10 parts water); the red shade changes to yellow, owing to the liberation of free alizarin, and after pouring the acid away from the sample and adding a little 2 per cent caustic soda solution, a violet solution is obtained.

TEST 4

If the dye is found in Test 3 to be a vat or sulphur dye, further distinctions can be made as follows:

A comparatively large sample of the dyed material (e.g. 1 in. square) is cut up into small pieces, or the individual threads separated; these are placed in a clean test tube. The material is just covered with a few ml of freshly prepared acid stannous chloride solution (10 g stannous chloride dissolved in 10 ml concentrated hydrochloric acid (30 per cent) and 5 ml water added). A clean filter paper is then wrapped over the mouth of the test tube so that the latter is completely covered, and two drops of normal lead acetate solution (19 g $Pb(CH_3COO)_2 3H_2O$ dissolved in 100 ml water) are placed on the paper. The contents of the test tube are next warmed gently and allowed to stand for a few minutes. In this treatment *sulphur* dyes are generally reduced to yellow or yellow–brown products and hydrogen sulphide is evolved, which forms a black or dark brown stain of lead sulphide on the filter paper. The solution must not be heated too strongly as a vigorous evolution of hydrochloric acid gas from the solution may prevent the formation of, or dissolve, the lead sulphide stain.

TEST 5

If the dyeing under examination appears to be a vat dye, confirmation may often be obtained by boiling a sample in the acid hydrosulphite reagent. As has been already described, the colour of the free leuco-compound of vat dye is frequently distinct from that of the sodium salt of the leuco-compound (alkaline "vat"), and this test is particularly useful for certain blues or blacks, where it is often difficult to distinguish the difference in colour of the alkaline "vat" from that of the original dyeing.

TEST 6

In the examination of certain types of materials, colouring matters involving metallic ions may be encountered. *Alizarin* blue is generally dyed (or printed) on a chromium mordant; *mineral khaki* dyeings contain chromium and iron; *cutch* dyeings contain chromium and copper, and certain tinted shades are produced by iron compounds. Chromium and copper may also both be present in *sulphur* dyeings (which are frequently after-treated with chromium and copper compounds). *Sulphur* dyeings are, however, detected by Test 4 above. In cases where the presence of such colouring matters is suspected, tests for the metals should be carried out as follows:

Copper. A sample of the material is placed in a clean porcelain dish and a few drops of concentrated hydrochloric acid added. After warming gently, 2–5 ml water are added and the solution made alkaline with ammonia. The contents of the dish are boiled and filtered into another dish (to remove iron, chromium or aluminium compounds), and a few drops of 0·1 per cent sodium diethyldithiocarbamate solution added to the filtrate (or to a portion of the filtrate). The production of a brown colour and precipitate indicate the presence of copper. It is advisable to carry out this test side by side with a test on a reference sample known to have been treated with a copper compound.

Iron. A sample of the material is placed in a clean porcelain dish and wetted with 2–3 drops of concentrated hydrochloric acid. The dish is warmed gently and a few millilitres of freshly prepared 1 per cent potassium ferrocyanide solution added. The production of a blue colour indicates the presence of iron.

Chromium. A sample of the material is ashed on a porcelain crucible lid and a small crystal of potassium chlorate added to the ash. The production of a yellow fused mass indicates the presence of chromium, which may be confirmed by the modified lead chromate test described by Clayton.[4] It is preferable to carry out a control test on a reference sample at the same time.

In the case of *Alizarin blue* a blue–red reduction compound marking-off on to the bleached material is obtained in Test 3 above, which distinguishes it from blue vat dyes (see Table IV, p. 38). The stain re-oxidizes in air to a blue shade, greener than the original blue shade. The presence of a definite amount of chromium provides confirmatory evidence. Traces of chromium may sometimes be found in vat dyeings which have been oxidized by means of dichromate solutions.

TEST 7

In the examination of black-dyed materials the following types of black dyes may be encountered, and their respective behaviour in Test 3 is given in brackets:

Reactive blacks (which give coloured reduction products, and do not re-oxidize to black in air). They are identified in Test 1.

Vat blacks (which give red, violet, blue or yellow "vats").

Sulphur blacks, including indocarbons (which give yellow or brown–yellow "vats").

Azoic blacks, *Direct blacks*, After-treated or developed *Direct blacks* (which give yellow or colourless reduction products and do not re-oxidize to black in air)

Aniline black (which gives a brown stain, re-oxidizing to black in air).

Logwood black (which gives a yellow stain in Test 2 and Test 3, but the stain does not re-oxidize to black in air).

A vat black should be confirmed by Test 5 (acid hydrosulphite); a sulphur black should be confirmed by Test 4 (acid stannous chloride).

Aniline black should be confirmed by placing a small sample of the dyed or printed material in cold dilute nitric acid (1 part concentrated nitric acid and 1 part water, by volume); after about 30 sec immersion yellow–brown oxidation products bleed away from the sample into the acid. A reference dyeing or print of Aniline black should be tested side by side with the unknown sample. Alternatively, the presence of Aniline black may be confirmed by boiling a sample of the dyeing in sodium hyporchlorite solution, when the colour of the material changes to brown.

Logwood black should be confirmed by placing a sample of the material in cold dilute hydrochloric acid (1 part concentrated hydrochloric acid and 1 part water, by volume); the sample turns red almost at once and the red colour bleeds into the acid. Logwood black is generally dyed on an iron mordant, although for some shades of black, both iron and chromium mordants may be used together. The metals may be identified by the tests given above.

Identification of "Direct-dyeing" and "Oxidized" Black Vat Dyes. Test 3 may be used for distinguishing between direct-dyeing black vat dyes, e.g. Caledon Direct Black R and oxidized black vat dyes, e.g. Caledon Black NB. The latter type are green dyes, oxidized on the fibre to black by treatment with sodium hypochlorite solution. Consequently, in Test 3, the latter type mark-off on to the bleached material and the stain re-oxidizes in the air to the original green shade, which may then be oxidized to black by treatment in sodium hypochlorite solution containing 1·5 g available chlorine per litre.

Mixtures of Vat Dyes. In cases where the components of a mixture shade have not been well chosen, as when the component dyes have a wide difference in vatting or in exhaustion properties, it is frequently possible to obtain evidence as to the identity of each component, and even to obtain some degree of separation. Test 3 may be used for this purpose. Certain mixture shades have been examined, which when wrapped up tightly in bleached linen or cotton material and boiled in the alkaline hydrosulphite reagent, mark-off to give an unlevel stain. When the components give distinctively coloured "vats", local differences in the colour of the stain may be observed immediately on opening the roll of bleached material. After allowing the stain to re-oxidize in the air, local differences in colour may still be evident and an indication of the colours of the component dyes obtained.

This test may be carried further if desired by using a range of reducing or marking-off conditions, decreasing in severity from 2 per cent caustic soda solution containing 5 per cent sodium hydrosulphite at the boil to a solution containing 1 per cent soda ash and 0·1 per cent dextrose at 75°C or 60°C. The conditions of marking-off may be controlled so as to obtain the maximum separation of the component dyes.

Mixtures of Vat and Direct Dyes. Dyeings have been examined which were essentially vat dyed, but contained a small fraction of direct shading or topping colour. Such direct dyes may be detected in Test 2, as they bleed on to bleached material when boiled in water. As the direct dye is usually present in only a small proportion, the stain on the bleached material may be very faint; a more definite stain may be obtained in the case of piece dyeings by reversing the procedure and wrapping a small sample of bleached cotton or linen in the dyed material. In confirmation the stained material may be boiled in the alkaline hydrosulphite reagent, permanent decolorization of the stain indicating the presence of a direct dye.

REFERENCES

1. I.C.I. Ltd. Technical Information, Dyehouse No. 445, 1958.
2. JORDINSON, F. and LOCKWOOD, R., *J.S..D.C.*, **78,** 122 (1962).
3. JORDINSON, F. and LOCKWOOD, R., *J.S.D.C.*, **80,** 202 (1964).
4. CLAYTON, E., *J.S.D.C.*, **53,** 380 (1937).

Chapter 5 IDENTIFICATION OF INDANTHRONE BLUE DYES

As MENTIONED on p. 8 nitric acid gives valuable distinctions between members of families of dyes such as the indanthrone and indigo types of blue vat dyes. Dyes produced by halogenation of indanthrone are oxidised by nitric acid to yellow products, which are readily converted back to the blue dyes by mild reduction treatment. The parent indanthrone (Caledon Blue XRN) is itself readily oxidized, but the halogenated derivatives, e.g. Caledon Blue XRC, are less readily oxidized and the resistance to oxidation varies with each particular product. Concentrated nitric acid as used in the tests already described, is a sufficiently powerful oxidizing agent to oxidize all the halogenated products immediately to yellow. If, however, a milder oxidizing agent is used, distinctions in the relative rate of oxidation of members of this group of blue dyes can be made. For instance, with dyeings of Caledon Blue XRN and Caledon Blue XRC, placed together in a suitable oxidizing solution, it is possible to oxidize the former to yellow, while the latter will change only to green–blue indicating that comparatively little oxidation has occurred.

The rate of oxidation (or greening) of all the available blue dyes in this group has been examined, and the dyes have been classified into four main sub-divisions, as shown in Table VIII. For this purpose two solutions of nitric acid are necessary, viz.

Solution (i) – 1 part, by volume, concentrated nitric acid and 1 part water.

Solution (ii) – 3 parts, by volume, concentrated nitric acid and 1 part water.

These solutions are cooled to room temperature and used as described in Test III (see p. 6.).

The generalization may be made that dyes in Groups C and D should be regarded as of good fastness to oxidizing treatments (e.g. hypochlorite treatments in bleaching), whereas dyes in Groups A and B may be regarded as dyes of less satisfactory fastness. A rapid test suitable for

TABLE VIII. *Classification of Indanthrone Blues according to the Nitric Acid Test*

	Colour after 15 sec immersion	
	Pale shades	Medium or deep shades
Solution (i)		
Group A	Yellow–green	Green
Group B	Green	Blue–green
Group C	Blue–green	Blue
Group D	Blue–green	Blue
Solution (ii)		
Group A	Yellow (immediately)	
Group B	Yellow (immediately)	
Group C	Green–yellow	
Group D	Green	

all practical purposes is thus to use Solution (i) alone; if the sample does not turn green within 15 sec, it may be regarded as of good fastness to "greening" in bleaching treatments.

The differentiation between dyes of Groups A and B and dyes of Groups C and D may be confirmed by the acid hydrosulphite test e.g. Caledon Blues 3G, XRN and GCP give a violet colour in Test II, while Caledon Blues GCX and XRC remain blue (see Table IV).

Table IX shows the commercial names of the blue indanthrone dyes in the four groups.

The following are points of importance which should be noted before employing this test.

Depth of Shade. The resistance to oxidation as observed in the test is dependent on the depth of shade of the dyeing under examination. Pale shades are oxidized more rapidly than deep shades of the same dye. It is therefore necessary whenever possible to test an unknown dyeing side by side with control samples of about the same depth as the unknown, preferably with a control sample of at least one dye from each of the four groups in Table IX.

Temperature of Dyeing. The resistance to oxidation is influenced by the temperature at which the shade has been dyed. Caledon Blue XRN

TABLE IX. *Classification of Blue Dyes Derived from Indanthrone*

	Group A	Group B	Group C	Group D
Alizanthrene				Blue RC
Anthrasol				Blue IBC
Benzadone		Blue GCD Blue RS		Blue RC
Caledon	Blue 3G Brilliant Blue3G	Blue GCP Blue XRN Brilliant Blue RN	Blue GXD	Blue XRC
Cibanone	Blue F3G	Blue FGCD Blue FRS		Blue FGF
Cibantine				Blue FGF
Indanthren	Blue 3G Blue 5G Blue 3GN	Blue GCD Blue GCDN Blue GP Blue RS Blue RSN Brilliant Blue R	Blue BCS	Blue BC
Indigosol				Blue IBC
Paradone	Brilliant Blue3G	Blue GCP Blue RS Brilliant Blue R		
Sandothrene		Blue F-NGCD Blue F-NGCDN Blue F-NRSN		Blue NG
Sandozol				Blue F-BC
Tinon	Blue 3G-F	Blue GCP-F Blue RS-F Blue RSN-F	Blue GCD	Blue GF-F Blue GL-F
Tinosol				Blue BC-F

(unhalogenated) is recommended by the manufacturers to be dyed at 60°C, but the halogenated products are recommended to be dyed at temperatures not higher than 50°C, since at higher temperatures loss of halogen occurs in the dyebath which is strongly alkaline, and the resistance to oxidation is consequently decreased. Experiments have been carried out with Caledon Blues (I.C.I.) to demonstrate this point, and it has been found that Caledon Blue 3G, and GCP when dyed at 60°C, have less resistance to oxidation, as observed in the nitric acid test, than when dyed at 50°C. Caledon Blue GCD and XRC showed little or no difference when dyed at 60°C, as these dyes have a comparatively high resistance to oxidation. These experiments were made with full shades of the dyes referred to above and it was considered that, although the dyeings of Caledon Blue 3G, and GCP, at 60°C, had suffered a decrease in resistance to oxidation, the decrease was not sufficiently great to interfere with the classification of these dyes as given in Table IX. For instance, Caledon Blue GCP (Group B) was still distinct, in the nitric acid test, from Caledon Blue 3G (Group A). It is, however, possible that with pale shades dyed at 60°C it would be difficult to make these distinctions.

Examination of Shades restored by Hydrosulphite. As has been stated above, the greening of these dyes in oxidizing treatments can be reversed, and the blue shade restored, by a mild reducing treatment. The dye manufacturers recommend a dilute solution of sodium hydrosulphite for this purpose (2½ oz per 100 gal). Experiments have been made with the dyeings of Caledon colours described under (ii) above, in order to examine the behaviour in the nitric acid tests of dyeings which have been "greened" by an oxidizing treatment (15 min in acid hypochlorite solution, pH 5·0, 1·5 g available chlorine per litre) and subsequently re-converted to the blue shades by a reduction treatment with sodium hydrosulphite solution. The resistance to oxidation of dyeings of Caledon Blue XRN, GCP, GCX, and RC, whether dyed at 50°C or at 60°C was not noticeably affected. With dyeings of Caledon Blue 3GS there was a decrease in the resistance to oxidation.

A similar grouping of the indanthrone blue dyes is obtained with the acid permanganate test. The colours range from green–yellow to green–blue depending on the resistance to oxidation of the dye.

Tinon Blue GCD (Geigy) is grouped in the colour index with C.I. Vat Blue 14. Tests II, III, and V, however, show that it behaves more like C.I. Vat Blue 10, and, accordingly it has been listed as similar to C.I. Vat Blue 10. Tinon Blue GCP-F (Geigy) which is not listed in the colour index shows colour reactions in all the tests similar to those dyes listed under C.I. Vat Blue 14, and it has been listed as "similar to" C.I. Vat Blue 14. These are the only cases where groups of synonymous dyes do not correspond with the colour index groups.

Chapter 6 IDENTIFICATION OF INDIGO BLUE DYES

In the case of indigo blue dyes (indigo and halogenation products of indigo) distinctions can be made by means of nitric acid in a similar manner to that already described for the indanthren blues derived from indanthrone. Indigo blues give yellow oxidation products, and in concentrated nitric acid a series of colour changes from blue through brown–green and green to yellow may be observed. The resistance to oxidation increases with the degree of halogenation. Concentrated nitric acid is used as described for Test III (see p. 6).

This family of dyes may be placed in the following order of increasing resistance to oxidation from indigo itself up to the most highly halogenated product, Indigo 6B:

Indigo
Indigo Ciba R
Indigo 2R
BASF Brilliant Indigo BB
BASF Brilliant Indigo 4B
BASF Brilliant Indigo 6B

The dyeing under examination, if found by means of the five tests to be a blue of the indigo type (see Table IV, p. 38) should be tested in concentrated nitric acid side by side with control samples of similar shades of as many of the indigo blue dyes above as are available.

INDEX OF VAT DYES

No.	Table No.	Name of dye (with manufacturer's initials)	
95	I	Algol Orange RF	(CFM)
420	II	Algol Scarlet GGN	(CFM)
395	II	Algol Scarlet RB	(CFM)
720	IV	Alizanthrene Blue RC	(ICI)
775	IV	Alizanthrene Navy Blue R	(ICI)
775	IV	Alizanthrene Navy Blue RT	(ICI)
1515	VII	Anthra Grey BT	(BASF)
35	I	Anthra Yellow GC	(BASF)
815	IV	Anthrasol O	(FH)
855	IV	Anthrasol O4B	(FH)
865	IV	Anthrasol O4G	(FH)
45	I	Anthrasol Brilliant Orange IRK	(FH)
410	II	Anthrasol Brilliant Pink I3B	(FH)
560	III	Anthrasol Brilliant Violet I4R	(FH)
840	IV	Anthrasol Bluc AGG	(FH)
720	IV	Anthrasol Blue IBC	(FH)
1745	VII	Anthrasol Blue Black IRD	(FH)
1295	VI	Anthrasol Brown IBR	(FH)
1280	VI	Anthrasol Brown IRRD	(FH)
130	I	Anthrasol Golden Yellow GK	(FH)
5	I	Anthrasol Golden Yellow IRK	(FH)
960	V	Anthrasol Green IB	(FH)
975	V	Anthrasol Green IGG	(FH)
1125	V	Anthrasol Green I3G	(FH)
1720	VII	Anthrasol Grey IBL	(FH)
1205	V	Anthrasol Grey IT	(FH)
1045	V	Anthrasol Olive Green IB	(FH)
1060	V	Anthrasol Olive Green IRB	(FH)
95	I	Anthrasol Orange HR	(FH)
380	II	Anthrasol Pink IR	(FH)
1715	VII	Anthrasol Printing Black IB	(FH)
1760	VII	Anthrasol Printing Black IGR	(FH)
840	IV	Anthrasol Printing Blue IGG	(FH)
595	III	Anthrasol Printing Violet IBBF	(FH)
580	III	Anthrasol Printing Violet IRR	(FH)
155	I	Anthrasol Printing Yellow 4G	(FH)
130	I	Anthrasol Printing Yellow IGOK	(FH)
525	II	Anthrasol Red IFBB	(FH)
370	II	Anthrasol Red Violet IRH	(FH)
395	II	Anthrasol Scarlet HB	(FH)
355	II	Anthrasol Scarlet IB	(FH)
595	III	Anthrasol Violet ABBF	(FH)
580	III	Anthrasol Violet ARR	(FH)
100	I	Anthrasol Yellow HCG	(FH)
115	I	Anthrasol Yellow I3R	(FH)
60	I	Anthrasol Yellow V	(FH)
850	IV	BASF Brilliant Indigo B	(BASF)

No.	Table No.	Name of dye (with manufacturer's initials)	
830	IV	BASF Brilliant Indigo BB	(BASF)
855	IV	BASF Brilliant Indigo 4B	(BASF)
855	IV	BASF Brilliant Indigo 4BC	(BASF)
850	IV	BASF Brilliant Indigo BR	(BASF)
865	IV	BASF Brilliant Indigo 4G	(BASF)
1590	VII	Benzadone Black NB	(YDC)
735	IV	Benzadone Blue 3G	(YDC)
710	IV	Benzadone Blue GCD	(YDC)
720	IV	Benzadone Blue RC	(YDC)
740	IV	Benzadone Blue RLC	(YDC)
705	IV	Benzadone Blue RS	(YDC)
20	I	Benzadone Brilliant Orange 4R	(YDC)
555	III	Benzadone Brilliant Purple 2R	(YDC)
560	III	Benzadone Brilliant Purple 4R	(YDC)
550	III	Benzadone Brilliant Violet 3B	(YDC)
555	III	Benzadone Brilliant Violet 2RBF	(YDC)
1295	VI	Benzadone Brown BR	(YDC)
1315	VI	Benzadone Brown 2G	(YDC)
1350	VI	Benzadone Brown GB	(YDC)
1325	VI	Benzadone Brown R	(YDC)
630	IV	Benzadone Dark Blue BMS	(YDC)
630	IV	Benzadone Dark Blue BOA	(YDC)
630	IV	Benzadone Dark Blue BOR	(YDC)
680	IV	Benzadone Dark Blue G	(YDC)
1505	VII	Benzadone Direct Black 2G	(YDC)
1500	VII	Benzadone Direct Black R	(YDC)

No.	Table No.	Name of dye (with manufacturer's initials)	
1515	VII	Benzadone Direct Black RB	(YDC)
10	I	Benzadone Gold Orange G	(YDC)
130	I	Benzadone Gold Yellow GK	(YDC)
5	I	Benzadone Gold Yellow RK	(YDC)
1020	V	Benzadone Green 2B	(YDC)
1015	V	Benzadone Green BN	(YDC)
1690	VII	Benzadone Grey B	(YDC)
1580	VII	Benzadone Grey 3B	(YDC)
1685	VII	Benzadone Grey G	(YDC)
1675	VII	Benzadone Grey M	(YDC)
1670	VII	Benzadone Grey R	(YDC)
960	V	Benzadone Jade Green B	(YDC)
975	V	Benzadone Jade Green 2G	(YDC)
985	V	Benzadone Jade Green 4G	(YDC)
960	V	Benzadone Jade Green XN	(YDC)
960	V	Benzadone Jade Green XBN	(YDC)
780	IV	Benzadone Navy Blue R	(YDC)
1160	V	Benzadone Olive R	(YDC)
1205	V	Benzadone Olive T	(YDC)
1045	V	Benzadone Olive Green B	(YDC)
25	I	Benzadone Orange 2RT	(YDC)
525	II	Benzadone Red FBB	(YDC)
480	II	Benzadone Red 5G	(YDC)
545	III	Benzadone Violet B	(YDC)
145	I	Benzadone Yellow 5GK	(YDC)
905	IV	Benzindone Blue 2B	(YDC)
1280	VI	Benzindone Brown G	(YDC)
1590	VII	Caledon Black 2BM	(ICI)
1590	VII	Caledon Black NB	(ICI)
695	IV	Caledon Blue 3G	(ICI)
710	IV	Caledon Blue GCP	(ICI)
715	IV	Caledon Blue GXD	(ICI)

No.	Table No.	Name of dye (with manufacturer's initials)
1095	V	Caledon Olive OMW (ICI)
1160	V	Caledon Olive R (ICI)
1100	V	Caledon Olive RMW (ICI)
1045	V	Caledon Olive Green B (ICI)
25	I	Caledon Orange 2RT (ICI)
1455	VI	Caledon Orange Brown 2G (ICI)
305	II	Caledon Pink RL (ICI)
1610	VII	Caledon Printing Black R (ICI)
1640	VII	Caledon Printing Black 2R (ICI
695	IV	Caledon Printing Blue 3G (ICI)
1490	VI	Caledon Printing Brown 4R (ICI)
1250	VI	Caledon Printing Brown 01385 (ICI)
1800	VII	Caledon Printing Grey B (ICI)
1025	V	Caledon Printing Jade Green 5G (ICI)
680	IV	Caledon Printing Navy G (ICI)
760	IV	Caledon Printing Navy X (ICI)
45	I	Caledon Printing Orange 6R (ICI)
525	II	Caledon Printing Red 3B (ICI)
280	II	Caledon Printing Scarlet FR (ICI)
160	I	Caledon Printing Yellow 6G (ICI)
130	I	Caledon Printing Yellow GK (ICI)
30	I	Caledon Printing Yellow GW (ICI)
500	II	Caledon Red 4B (ICI)
245	II	Caledon Red BN (ICI)
485	II	Caledon Red 5G (ICI)
240	II	Caledon Red 2GN (ICI)
340	II	Caledon Red X5B (ICI)
275	II	Caledon Red Violet 2RN (ICI)
475	II	Caledon Rubine B (ICI)
575	III	Caledon Violet XBN (ICI)
80	I	Caledon Yellow 4G (ICI)
35	I	Caledon Yellow 5G (ICI)
145	I	Caledon Yellow 5GK (ICI)
190	I	Caledon Yellow 4GL (ICI)
65	I	Caledon Yellow GN (ICI)
165	I	Caledon Yellow 2R (ICI)
115	I	Caledon Yellow 3R (ICI)
180	I	Caledon Yellow Brown 3G (ICI)
425	II	Ciba Bordeaux F2RN (CIBA)
855	IV	Ciba Blue 2B (CIBA)
850	IV	Ciba Blue BR (CIBA)
890	IV	Ciba Blue RH (CIBA)
885	IV	Ciba Blue 2RH (CIBA)
895	IV	Ciba Blue 3RH (CIBA)
390	II	Ciba Brilliant Pink B (CIBA)
410	II	Ciba Brilliant Pink F3B (CIBA)
380	II	Ciba Brilliant Pink FR (CIBA)
1285	VI	Ciba Brown F2B (CIBA)
1475	VI	Ciba Brown FCH (CIBA)
1280	VI	Ciba Brown FG (CIBA)
1300	VI	Ciba Brown FV (CIBA)
95	I	Ciba Orange R (CIBA)
365	II	Ciba Pink B (CIBA)
1650	VII	Ciba Printing Black BDN (CIBA)
1220	VII	Ciba Printing Black FBL (CIBA)
1655	VII	Ciba Printing Black FTL (CIBA)
1665	VII	Ciba Printing Deep Black BD (CIBA)
405	II	Ciba Red F2B (CIBA)
370	II	Ciba Red F3BN (CIBA)
395	II	Ciba Scarlet BG (CIBA)
355	II	Ciba Scarlet F3B (CIBA)
255	II	Ciba Scarlet FG (CIBA)
590	III	Ciba Violet F6R (CIBA)
1590	VII	Cibanone Black F2B (CIBA)
1540	VII	Cibanone Black FBA (CIBA)

No.	Table No.	Name of dye (with manufacturer's initials)	No.	Table No.	Name of dye (with manufacturer's initials)
775	IV	Cibanone Navy Blue FRA (CIBA)	90	I	Cibanone Yellow FLGR (CIBA)
1045	V	Cibanone Olive FB (CIBA)	115	I	Cibanone Yellow F3R (CIBA)
1060	V	Cibanone Olive F2B (CIBA)			
1050	V	Cibanone Olive FBG (CIBA)	115	I	Cibanone Yellow F3RF (CIBA)
1110	V	Cibanone Olive FB2G (CIBA)	35	I	Cibanone Yellow GC (CIBA)
1080	V	Cibanone Olive F2G (CIBA)	105	I	Cibanone Yellow 2GR (CIBA)
1160	V	Cibanone Olive F2R (CIBA)			
1205	V	Cibanone Olive FS (CIBA)	225	I	Cibanone Yellow 2GW (CIBA)
20	I	Cibanone Orange F8R (CIBA)	1340	VI	Cibanone Yellow Brown FG (CIBA)
110	I	Cibanone Orange 6R (CIBA)			
1620	VII	Cibanone Printing Black F2B (CIBA)	855	IV	Cibantine Blue 2B (CIBA)
			720	IV	Cibantine Blue FGF (CIBA)
1625	VII	Cibanone Printing Black FN (CIBA)	960	V	Cibantine Brilliant Green FBF (CIBA)
625	III	Cibanone Printing Blue FCBN (CIBA)	45	I	Cibantine Brilliant Orange FRK (CIBA)
1265	VI	Cibanone Printing Brown F2R (CIBA)	380	II	Cibantine Brilliant Pink FR (CIBA)
1445	VI	Cibanone Printing Brown F3R (CIBA)	560	III	Cibantine Brilliant Violet F4R (CIBA)
525	II	Cibanone Red FBB (CIBA)	1440	VI	Cibantine Brown F3B (CIBA)
310	II	Cibanone Red F3B (CIBA)			
510	II	Cibanone Red F4B (CIBA)	1295	VI	Cibantine Brown FBR (CIBA)
300	II	Cibanone Red F6B (CIBA)			
245	II	Cibanone Red FRK (CIBA)	25	I	Cibantine Golden Orange F2R (CIBA)
445	II	Cibanone Red G (CIBA)			
1480	VI	Cibanone Red Brown RRF (CIBA)	130	I	Cibantine Golden Yellow FGK (CIBA)
550	III	Cibanone Violet F6B (CIBA)	5	I	Cibantine Golden Yellow FRK (CIBA)
575	III	Cibanone Violet FFB (CIBA)			
555	III	Cibanone Violet F2RB (CIBA)	1720	VII	Cibantine Grey FBL (CIBA)
			1755	VII	Cibantine Grey F3G (CIBA)
560	III	Cibanone Violet F4R (CIBA)	1045	V	Cibantine Olive FB (CIBA)
190	I	Cibanone Yellow F2G (CIBA)	1060	V	Cibantine Olive F2B (CIBA)
			95	I	Cibantine Orange R (CIBA)
210	I	Cibanone Yellow FGK (CIBA)	1700	VII	Cibantine Printing Black BM (CIBA)
230	I	Cibanone Yellow F2GK (CIBA)	525	II	Cibantine Red FBB (CIBA)
			395	II	Cibantine Scarlet 2B (CIBA)
145	I	Cibanone Yellow F5GK (CIBA)	355	II	Cibantine Scarlet F3B (CIBA)
65	I	Cibanone Yellow FGN (CIBA)	195	I	Cibantine Yellow F2G (CIBA)

No.	Table No.	Name of dye (with manufacturer's initials)
60	I	Cibantine Yellow V (CIBA)
1730	VII	Durindone Black BNP (ICI)
855	IV	Durindone Blue 4BC (ICI)
1280	VI	Durindone Brown G (ICI)
405	II	Durindone Magenta B (ICI)
95	I	Durindone Orange R (ICI)
430	II	Durindone Printing Pink 2B (ICI)
390	II	Durindone Pink FB (ICI)
380	II	Durindone Pink FF (ICI)
1740	VII	Durindone Printing Black AN (ICI)
1720	VII	Durindone Printing Black BL (ICI)
1695	VII	Durindone Printing Black G (ICI)
1655	VII	Durindone Printing Black TL (ICI)
355	II	Durindone Printing Scarlet R (ICI)
356	II	Durindone Red B (ICI)
370	II	Durindone Red 3B (ICI)
395	II	Durindone Scarlet 2B (ICI)
400	II	Durindone Scarlet 3B (ICI)
440	II	Durindone Scarlet 2GN (ICI)
255	II	Durindone Scarlet Y (ICI)
5	I	Estersol Golden Yellow IRK (LBH)
960	V	Estersol Green IB (LBH)
1720	VII	Estersol Grey IBL (LBH)
875	IV	Hydron Blue B (CFM)
870	IV	Hydron Blue G (CFM)
880	IV	Hydron Blue GG (CFM)
885	IV	Hydron Blue R (CFM)
900	IV	Hydron Blue RR (CFM)
895	IV	Hydron Blue 3R (CFM)
900	IV	Hydron Blue 3RN (CFM)
920	IV	Hydron Navy Blue CN (CFM)
1590	VII	Indanthren Black BB (BASF)
1485	VI	Indanthren Black Brown NT (CFM)
1485	VI	Indanthren Black Brown NTS (CFM)
1220	VI	Indanthren Black Brown R (FH)
1240	VI	Indanthren Black Brown RV (BASF)
720	IV	Indanthren Blue BC (BASF)
720	IV	Indanthren Blue BCS (BASF)
810	IV	Indanthren Blue BP (CFM)
660	IV	Indanthren Blue CLB (BASF)
935	IV	Indanthren Blue CLF (BASF)
635	IV	Indanthren Blue CLG (BASF)
640	IV	Indanthren Blue EB (FBy)
645	IV	Indanthren Blue ER (FBy)
695	IV	Indanthren Blue 3G (BASF)
930	IV	Indanthren Blue 5G (FBy)
710	IV	Indanthren Blue GCD (BASF)
710	IV	Indanthren Blue GCDN (BASF)
700	IV	Indanthren Blue 3GF (BASF)
695	IV	Indanthren Blue 3GN (BASF)
705	IV	Indanthren Blue GP (BASF)
790	IV	Indanthren Blue HCBG (FH)
755	IV	Indanthren Blue HCBR (FH)
655	IV	Indanthren Blue HCGK (FH)
650	IV	Indanthren Blue HCRK (FH)
705	IV	Indanthren Blue RS (BASF)
705	IV	Indanthren Blue RSN (BASF)
735	IV	Indanthren Blue Green FFB (BASF)
1030	V	Indanthren Blue Green H4B (FH)
490	II	Indanthren Bordeaux B (BASF)
330	II	Indanthren Bordeaux HRR (FH)
330	II	Indanthren Bordeaux RR (FH)

No.	Table No.	Name of dye (with manufacturer's initials)		No.	Table No.	Name of dye (with manufacturer's initials)	
695	IV	Indanthren Brilliant Blue 3G	(BASF)	380	II	Indanthren Brilliant Pink RS	(CFM)
705	IV	Indanthren Brilliant Blue R	(BASF)	360	II	Indanthren Brilliant Rubine RB	(CFM)
720	IV	Indanthren Brilliant Blue RCL	(BASF)	360	II	Indanthren Brilliant Rubine RBS	(CFM)
960	V	Indanthren Brilliant Green B	(BASF)	505	II	Indanthren Brilliant Scarlet EFR	(FBy)
965	V	Indanthren Brilliant Green 3B	(BASF)	265	II	Indanthren Brilliant Scarlet E3G	(FBy)
960	V	Indanthren Brilliant Green FFB	(BASF)	290	II	Indanthren Brilliant Scarlet FGC	(CFM)
985	V	Indanthren Brilliant Green 4G	(BASF)	520	II	Indanthren Brilliant Scarlet FR	(CFM)
975	V	Indanthren Brilliant Green 3GF	(BASF)	450	II	Indanthren Brilliant Scarlet RK	(BASF)
985	V	Indanthren Brilliant Green 4GF	(BASF)	550	III	Indanthren Brilliant Violet 3B	(BASF)
975	V	Indanthren Brilliant Green GG	(BASF)	605	III	Indanthren Brilliant Violet BBK	(FBy)
1120	V	Indanthren Brilliant Green H3G	(FH)	615	III	Indanthren Brilliant Violet E5R	(FBy)
40	I	Indanthren Brilliant Orange GK	(CFM)	560	III	Indanthren Brilliant Violet 4R	(BASF)
70	I	Indanthren Brilliant Orange GR	(FH)	600	III	Indanthren Brilliant Violet RK	(FBy)
45	I	Indanthren Brilliant Orange RK	(CFM)	555	III	Indanthren Brilliant Violet RR	(BASF)
45	I	Indanthren Brilliant Orange RKN	(CFM)	1415	VI	Indanthren Bronze GC	(CFM)
45	I	Indanthren Brilliant Orange RKS	(CFM)	1295	VI	Indanthren Brown BR	(FBy)
75	I	Indanthren Brilliant Orange RR	(FH)	1325	VI	Indanthren Brown FFR	(FBy)
390	II	Indanthren Brilliant Pink B	(CFM)	1375	VI	Indanthren Brown G	(FBy)
				1245	VI	Indanthren Brown GCW	(CFM)
410	II	Indanthren Brilliant Pink 3B	(CFM)	1315	VI	Indanthren Brown GG	(FBy)
285	II	Indanthren Brilliant Pink BL	(FBy)	1435	VI	Indanthren Brown GR	(FBy)
380	II	Indanthren Brilliant Pink R	(CFM)	1430	VI	Indanthren Brown 3GT	(FBy)
380	II	Indanthren Brilliant Pink RB	(CFM)	1385	VI	Indanthren Brown LG	(BASF)
380	II	Indanthren Brilliant Pink RP	(CFM)				

No.	Table No.	Name of dye (with manufacturer's initials)	No.	Table No.	Name of dye (with manufacturer's initials)
770	IV	Indanthren Navy Blue TRR (BASF)	1655	VII	Indanthren Printing Black TL (FH)
1180	V	Indanthren Olive EG (FBy)	810	IV	Indanthren Printing Blue BR (CFM)
1185	V	Indanthren Olive EGR (FBy)	840	IV	Indanthren Printing Blue GG (FH)
1150	V	Indanthren Olive 3G (FBy)	655	IV	Indanthren Printing Blue HFG (FH)
1190	V	Indanthren Olive 4G (FBy)	835	IV	Indanthren Printing Blue HR (FH)
1075	V	Indanthren Olive GG (CFM)	705	IV	Indanthren Printing Blue KRS (BASF)
1175	V	Indanthren Olive GR (BASF)	845	IV	Indanthren Printing Blue 3R (CFM)
1155	V	Indanthren Olive GRL (BASF)	1270	VI	Indanthren Printing Brown B (FH)
1070	V	Indanthren Olive HG (FH)	1305	VI	Indanthren Printing Brown BT (CFM)
1090	V	Indanthren Olive MW (BASF)	1265	VI	Indanthren Printing Brown HRR (FH)
1160	V	Indanthren Olive R (FBy)	1355	VI	Indanthren Printing Brown HTM (FH)
1105	V	Indanthren Olive RMW (BASF)	1290	VI	Indanthren Printing Brown R (FH)
1205	V	Indanthren Olive T (BASF)	1255	VI	Indanthren Printing Brown 5R (FH)
1045	V	Indanthren Olive Green B (BASF)	1410	VI	Indanthren Printing Brown RL (FBy)
1115	V	Indanthren Olive Green EBG (FBy)	1735	VII	Indanthren Printing Grey HGL (FH)
1055	V	Indanthren Olive Green GG (BASF)	795	IV	Indanthren Printing Navy Blue RR (BASF)
55	I	Indanthren Orange F3R (BASF)	1075	V	Indanthren Printing Olive GW (CFM)
235	I	Indanthren Orange GG (FBy)	360	II	Indanthren Printing Red 3B (CFM)
20	I	Indanthren Orange 4R (BASF)	255	II	Indanthren Printing Scarlet GG (FH)
120	I	Indanthren Orange 7RK (FBy)	595	III	Indanthren Printing Violet BBF (CFM)
215	I	Indanthren Orange RR (BASF)	550	III	Indanthren Printing Violet F3B (BASF)
25	I	Indanthren Orange RRTS (BASF)	560	III	Indanthren Printing Violet F4R (BASF)
1715	VII	Indanthren Printing Black B (FH)	585	III	Indanthren Printing Violet RF (CFM)
1660	VII	Indanthren Printing Black BGL (FH)			
1720	VII	Indanthren Printing Black BL (FH)			
1615	VII	Indanthren Printing Black BR (BASF)			
1795	VII	Indanthren Printing Black HC (FH)			

No.	Table No.	Name of dye (with manufacturer's initials)		No.	Table No.	Name of dye (with manufacturer's initials)	
180	I	Indanthren Yellow		1720	VII	Indigosol Grey	
		Brown 3G	(FBy)			IBL(F)	(DH)
1195	V	Indanthren Yellow		1755	VII	Indigosol Grey	
		Green GC	(CFM)			I3F(F)	(DH)
815	IV	Indigo		1205	V	Indigosol Grey	
825	IV	Indigo 2R	(ICI)			ISG(F)	(DH)
815	IV	Indigo Ciba	(CIBA)	1045	V	Indigosol Olive	
820	IV	Indigo Ciba R	(CIBA)			Green IB(F)	(DH)
825	IV	Indigo Ciba 2R	(CIBA)	1065	V	Indigosol Olive	
815	IV	Indigosol O	(DH)			Green IBU(F)	(DH)
855	IV	Indigosol O4B	(DH)	95	I	Indigosol Orange HR	(DH)
860	IV	Indigosol O6B	(DH)	20	I	Indigosol Orange	
820	IV	Indigosol OR	(DH)			I8R (F)	(DH)
840	IV	Indigosol Blue AGG	(DH)	380	II	Indigosol Pink IR(F)	(DH)
720	IV	Indigosol Blue		840	IV	Indigosol Printing	
		IBC (F)	(DH)			Blue IGG	(DH)
425	II	Indigosol Bordeaux		1710	VII	Indigosol Printing	
		I2RN	(DH)			Black AB2N	(DH)
45	I	Indigosol Brilliant		1630	VII	Indigosol Printing	
		Orange IRK (F)	(DH)			Black BZ	(DH)
410	II	Indigosol Brilliant		590	III	Indigosol Printing	
		Pink I3B (F)	(DH)			Purple IR	(DH)
560	III	Indigosol Brilliant		595	III	Indigosol Printing	
		Violet I4R (F)	(DH)			Violet IBBF	(DH)
565	III	Indigosol Brilliant		580	III	Indigosol Printing	
		Violet I2RB (F)	(DH)			Violet IRR	(DH)
1440	VI	Indigosol Brown		590	III	Indigosol Purple AR	(DH)
		I3B (F)	(DH)	350	II	Indigosol Red AB	(DH)
1295	VI	Indigosol Brown		375	II	Indigosol Red I2B(F)	(DH)
		IBR (F)	(DH)	525	II	Indigosol Red	
1280	VI	Indigosol Brown				IFBB(F)	(DH)
		IRRD (F)	(DF)	370	II	Indigosol Red	
1390	VI	Indigosol Brown				Violet IRH	(DH)
		IRV (F)	(DH)	535	III	Indigosol Red	
25	I	Indigosol Golden				Violet IRRL(F)	(DH)
		Orange I2R (F)	(DH)	295	II	Indigosol Rubine	
125	I	Indigosol Golden				IRB(F)	(DH)
		Yellow AR	(DH)	395	II	Indigosol Scarlet HB	(DH)
130	I	Indigosol Golden		355	II	Indigosol Scarlet	
		Yellow IGK (F)	(DH)			IB(F)	(DH)
5	I	Indigosol Golden		595	III	Indigosol Violet	
		Yellow IRK (F)	(DH)			ABBF	(DH)
960	V	Indigosol Green		580	III	Indigosol Violet	
		IB (F)	(DH)			ARR	(DH)
975	V	Indigosol Green		540	III	Indigosol Violet	
		IGG (F)	(DH)			I5R(F)	(DH)

No.	Table No.	Name of dye (with manufacturer's initials)	
210	I	Indigosol Yellow 2GB(F)	(DH)
100	I	Indigosol Yellow HCGN	(DH)
195	I	Indigosol Yellow I2G(F)	(DH)
150	I	Indigosol Yellow R(F)	(DH)
60	I	Indigosol Yellow V	(DH)
1590	II	Paradone Black AB New	(LBH)
715	IV	Paradone Blue GCD	(LBH)
710	IV	Paradone Blue GCP	(LBH)
720	IV	Paradone Blue RC	(LBH)
705	IV	Paradone Blue RS	(LBH)
735	IV	Paradone Blue Green FFB	(LBH)
330	II	Paradone Bordeaux RR	(LBH)
695	IV	Paradone Brilliant Blue 3G	(LBH)
705	IV	Paradone Brilliant Blue R	(LBH)
70	I	Paradone Brilliant Orange GR New	(LBH)
45	I	Paradone Brilliant Orange RK	(LBH)
380	II	Paradone Brilliant Pink R	(LBH)
525	II	Paradone Brilliant Red 3BS	(LBH)
525	II	Paradone Brilliant Red FBB	(LBH)
450	II	Paradone Brilliant Scarlet RK	(LBH)
545	III	Paradone Brilliant Violet B New	(LBH)
550	III	Paradone Brilliant Violet 3B	(LBH)
555	III	Paradone Brilliant Violet 2R	(LBH)
560	III	Paradone Brilliant Violet 4R	(LBH)
1315	VI	Paradone Brown 2G	(LBH)
1325	VI	Paradone Brown R	(LBH)
630	IV	Paradone Dark Blue	(LBH)
630	IV	Paradone Dark Blue 58321	(LBH)
775	IV	Paradone Dark Blue RFW	(LBH)
1530	VII	Paradone Direct Black BG	(LBH)
1525	VII	Paradone Direct Black RS New	(LBH)
10	I	Paradone Golden Orange G	(LBH)
130	I	Paradone Golden Yellow GK	(LBH)
5	I	Paradone Golden Yellow RK	(LBH)
30	I	Paradone Golden Yellow GW	(LBH)
940	V	Paradone Green G	(LBH)
945	V	Paradone Green 2G	(LBH)
1585	VII	Paradone Grey B	(LBH)
1580	VII	Paradone Grey 3B	(LBH)
1675	VII	Paradone Grey M	(LBH)
1680	VII	Paradone Grey MG	(LBH)
1585	VII	Paradone Grey R	(LBH)
960	V	Paradone Jade Green B New	(LBH)
960	V	Paradone Jade Green BX New	(LBH)
975	V	Paradone Jade Green 2G	(LBH)
985	V	Paradone Jade Green 4G	(LBH)
960	V	Paradone Jade Green XS New	(LBH)
680	IV	Paradone Navy Blue G	(LBH)
780	IV	Paradone Navy Blue R	(LBH)
705	IV	Paradone Printing Blue FRS	(LBH)
1465	VI	Paradone Printing Brown TM	(LBH)
1470	VI	Paradone Printing Brown TMI	(LBH)
1160	V	Paradone Olive R	(LBH)
1205	V	Paradone Olive T	(LBH)

No.	Table No.	Name of dye (with manufacturer's initials)	No.	Table No.	Name of dye (with manufacturer's initials)
1045	V	Paradone Olive Green B (LBH)	705	IV	Sandothrene Blue F-NRSN (S)
25	I	Paradone Orange RRT (LBH)	465	II	Sandothrene Bordeaux N2B (S)
1295	VI	Paradone Red Brown 2RD (LBH)	345	II	Sandothrene Bordeaux F-N2G
1400	VI	Paradone Red Brown 5RD (LBH)	960	V	Sandothrene Brilliant Green F-N2B (S)
325	II	Paradone Scarlet 2G (LBH)	990	V	Sandothrene Brilliant Green F-N4G (S)
270	II	Paradone Scarlet GK (LBH)			
65	I	Paradone Yellow G New (LBH)	975	V	Sandothrene Brilliant Green F-N2GF (S)
35	I	Paradone Yellow GC (LBH)	995	V	Sandothrene Brilliant Green F-N4GF (S)
35	I	Paradone Yellow GCX (LBH)	960	V	Sandothrene Brilliant Green F-NBF (S)
80	I	Paradone Yellow 4G (LBH)			
170	I	Paradone Yellow 4GF (LBH)	1000	V	Sandothrene Brilliant Green F-N5GF (S)
170	I	Paradone Yellow 8GF (LBH)	40	I	Sandothrene Brilliant Orange F-NGK (S)
145	I	Paradone Yellow 5GK (LBH)	45	I	Sandothrene Brilliant Orange F-NRK (S)
115	I	Paradone Yellow 3RT (LBH)	415	II	Sandothrene Brilliant Pink 2B (S)
1590	VII	Sandothrene Black F-N2B (S)	410	II	Sandothrene Brilliant Pink F-3B (S)
1595	VII	Sandothrene Black F-N2BA (S)	335	II	Sandothrene Brilliant Pink F-NG (S)
1595	VII	Sandothrene Black F-N3BA (S)	495	II	Sandothrene Brilliant Pink F-N2R (S)
1515	VII	Sandothrene Black F-NDRB (S)	380	II	Sandothrene Brilliant Pink F-R (S)
1535	VII	Sandothrene Black F-N2G (S)	1440	VI	Sandothrene Brown F-N3B (S)
1555	VII	Sandothrene Black F-NR (S)	1295	VI	Sandothrene Brown F-NBR (S)
720	IV	Sandothrene Blue NG (S)	1275	VI	Sandothrene Brown F-N2BR (S)
710	IV	Sandothrene Blue F-NGCD (S)	1280	VI	Sandothrene Brown F-G (S)
710	IV	Sandothrene Blue F-NGCDN (S)	1380	VI	Sandothrene Brown F-NG
735	IV	Sandothrene Blue F-N3G (S)	1375	VI	Sandothrene Brown F-NBG (S)
915	IV	Sandothrene Blue F-N4G (S)	1325	VI	Sandothrene Brown F-NR (S)

No.	Table No.	Name of dye (with manufacturer's initials)
1390	VI	Sandothrene Brown F-NRV (S)
1425	VI	Sandothrene Brown F-V (S)
250	II	Sandothrene Copper Red F-NR (S)
630	IV	Sandothrene Dark Blue F-NBOA (S)
630	IV	Sandothrene Dark Blue F-NMBA (S)
775	IV	Sandothrene Dark Blue F-NR (S)
785	IV	Sandothrene Dark Blue N2R (S)
10	I	Sandothrene Golden Orange F-NG (S)
175	I	Sandothrene Golden Orange F-N3G (S)
185	I	Sandothrene Golden Orange N2GT (S)
30	I	Sandothrene Golden Yellow F-NGW (S)
130	I	Sandothrene Golden Yellow NGK (S)
5	I	Sandothrene Golden Yellow F-NRK (S)
1210	V	Sandothrene Green F-N6G (S)
1785	VII	Sandothrene Grey F-NBG (S)
1750	VII	Sandothrene Grey F-N3G (S)
1645	VII	Sandothrene Grey F-N2GR (S)
1165	V	Sandothrene Khaki F-N2G (S)
1045	V	Sandothrene Olive F-N2B (S)
1050	V	Sandothrene Olive F-NBG (S)
1110	V	Sandothrene Olive F-NB2G (S)
1060	V	Sandothrene Olive F-NF2B (S)
1160	V	Sandothrene Olive F-N2R (S)
1205	V	Sandothrene Olive F-NT (S)
110	I	Sandothrene Orange N6R (S)
95	I	Sandothrene Orange R (S)
360	II	Sandothrene Pink BG (S)
1620	VII	Sandothrene Printing Black F-N2B (S)
1655	VII	Sandothrene Printing Black TL (S)
625	III	Sandothrene Printing Bluc F-NCBN (S)
805	IV	Sandothrene Printing Blue F-N2R (S)
405	II	Sandothrene Red F-2B (S)
370	II	Sandothrene Red F-3B (S)
310	II	Sandothrene Red F-N2B (S)
510	II	Sandothrene Red F-N4B (S)
300	II	Sandothrene Red F-N6B (S)
525	II	Sandothrene Red F-NF2B (S)
245	II	Sandothrene Red F-N2R (S)
445	II	Sandothrene Red NG (S)
1345	VI	Sandothrene Red Brown F-NR (S)
25	I	Sandothrene Red Orange F-NG (S)
20	I	Sandothrene Red Orange F-NR (S)
355	II	Sandothrene Scarlet F-3B (S)
550	III	Sandothrene Violet F-N3B (S)
560	III	Sandothrene Violet F-N4R (S)
555	III	Sandothrene Violet F-N2RB (S)

No.	Table No.	Name of dye (with manufacturer's initials)
570	III	Sandothrene Violet N2BW (S)
65	I	Sandothrene Yellow F-NG (S)
190	I	Sandothrene Yellow F-N2G (S)
230	I	Sandothrene Yellow F-N2GK (S)
145	I	Sandothrene Yellow F-N5GK (S)
210	I	Sandothrene Yellow F-NGKF (S)
65	I	Sandothrene Yellow F-NGN (S)
105	I	Sandothrene Yellow N2GR (S)
90	I	Sandothrene Yellow F-NLGR (S)
115	I	Sandothrene Yellow F-N3R (S)
35	I	Sandothrene Yellow NGC (S)
225	I	Sandothrene Yellow N2GW (S)
1340	VI	Sandothrene Yellow Brown F-NG (S)
720	IV	Sandozol Blue F-BC (S)
815	IV	Sandozol Blue O (S)
855	IV	Sandozol Blue O4B (S)
820	IV	Sandozol Blue OR (S)
425	II	Sandozol Bordeaux 2RN (S)
45	I	Sandozol Brilliant Orange F-RK (S)
435	II	Sandozol Brilliant Pink 5B (S)
410	II	Sandozol Brilliant Pink F-3B (S)
560	III	Sandozol Brilliant Violet F-4R (S)
1440	VI	Sandozol Brown F-3B (S)
1295	VI	Sandozol Brown F-BR (S)
1280	VI	Sandozol Brown F-RRD (S)
1390	VI	Sandozol Brown F-RV
25	I	Sandozol Golden Orange F-2R (S)
130	I	Sandozol Golden Yellow F-GK (S)
5	I	Sandozol Golden Yellow F-RK (S)
1960	V	Sandozol Green F-B (S)
1975	V	Sandozol Green F-2G (S)
1720	VII	Sandozol Grey F-BL (S)
1755	VII	Sandozol Grey F-3F (S)
1205	V	Sandozol Grey F-SG (S)
1045	V	Sandozol Olive Green F-B (S)
20	I	Sandozol Orange F-8R (S)
95	I	Sandozol Orange R (S)
380	II	Sandozol Pink F-R (S)
1705	VII	Sandozol Printing Black R (S)
840	IV	Sandozol Printing Blue F-2G (S)
590	III	Sandozol Printing Purple F-R (S)
595	III	Sandozol Printing Violet F-BBF (S)
350	II	Sandozol Red AB (S)
375	II	Sandozol F-2B (S)
525	II	Sandozol Red F-FBB (S)
370	II	Sandozol Red Violet F-RH (S)
395	II	Sandozol Scarlet B (S)
355	II	Sandozol Scarlet F-2B (S)
100	I	Sandozol Yellow CG (S)
195	I	Sandozol Yellow F-2G (S)
210	I	Sandozol Yellow F-2GB (S)
150	I	Sandozol Yellow F-R (S)

No.	Table No.	Name of dye (with manufacturer's initials)	
60	I	Sandozol Yellow V	(S)
855	IV	Soledon Blue 4BC	(ICI)
720	IV	Soledon Blue 2RC	(ICI)
45	I	Soledon Brilliant Orange 6R	(ICI)
560	III	Soledon Brilliant Purple 2R	(ICI)
1325	VI	Soledon Brown R	(ICI)
1295	VI	Soledon Dark Brown 3R	(ICI)
130	I	Soledon Golden Yellow GK	(ICI)
5	I	Soledon Golden Yellow RK	(ICI)
1045	V	Soledon Green G	(ICI)
1720	VII	Soledon Grey B	(ICI)
815	IV	Soledon Indigo LL	(ICI)
965	V	Soledon Jade Green 3B	(ICI)
975	V	Soledon Jade Green 2G	(ICI)
960	V	Soledon Jade Green X	(ICI)
1205	V	Soledon Olive D	(ICI)
95	I	Soledon Orange R	(ICI)
430	II	Soledon Pink 2B	(ICI)
380	II	Soledon Pink FF	(ICI)
525	II	Soledon Red 2B	(ICI)
370	II	Soledon Red 3B	(ICI)
395	II	Soledon Scarlet B	(ICI)
115	I	Soledon Yellow 3R	(ICI)
855	IV	Tetra Blue 2B	(S)
850	IV	Tetra Blue BR	(S)
820	IV	Tetra Blue R	(S)
425	II	Tetra Bordeaux F-2RN	(S)
1725	VII	Tetra Grey BL	(S)
1080	V	Tetra Olive F-N2G	(S)
1080	V	Tetra Olive F-NGR	(S)
365	II	Tetra Pink B	(S)
1720	VII	Tetra Printing Black F-BL	(S)
400	II	Tetra Scarlet 2B	(S)
395	II	Tetra Scarlet BG	(S)
385	II	Tetra Scarlet BGN	(S)
255	II	Tetra Scarlet F-G	(S)
590	III	Tetra Violet F-6R	(S)
855	IV	Tina Blue 2B	(Gy)
850	IV	Tina Blue BR	(Gy)
425	II	Tina Bordeaux 2RN-F	(Gy)
415	II	Tina Brilliant Pink 2B	(Gy)
380	II	Tina Brilliant Pink R-F	(Gy)
1285	VI	Tina Brown 2B-F	(Gy)
1280	VI	Tina Brown G-F	(Gy)
1300	VI	Tina Brown VD	(Gy)
1720	VII	Tina Grey BL	(Gy)
820	IV	Tina Indigo R	(Gy)
825	IV	Tina Indigo 2R	(Gy)
95	I	Tina Orange R	(Gy)
365	II	Tina Pink B	(Gy)
360	II	Tina Pink BG	(Gy)
1720	VII	Tina Printing Black BL-F	(Gy)
1655	VII	Tina Printing Black TL-F	(Gy)
405	II	Tina Red 2B-F	(Gy)
370	II	Tina Red 3B-F	(Gy)
400	II	Tina Scarlet 2B	(Gy)
355	II	Tina Scarlet 3B-F	(Gy)
395	II	Tina Scarlet BG	(Gy)
255	II	Tina Scarlet G-F	(Gy)
590	III	Tina Violet 6R-F	(Gy)
1595	VII	Tinon Black 3BA-F	(Gy)
1590	VII	Tinon Black 2B-F	(Gy)
1600	VII	Tinon Black CAC	(Gy)
715	IV	Tinon Blue GCD	(Gy)
710	III	Tinon Blue GCP-F	(Gy)
735	IV	Tinon Blue 3G-F	(Gy)
720	IV	Tinon Blue GF-F	(Gy)
720	IV	Tinon Blue GL-F	(Gy)
705	IV	Tinon Blue RS-F	(Gy)
705	IV	Tinon Blue RSN-F	(Gy)
465	II	Tinon Bordeaux 2B	(Gy)
345	II	Tinon Bordeaux 2G-F	(Gy)
960	V	Tinon Brilliant Green 2BF	(Gy)
960	V	Tinon Brilliant Green BF-F	(Gy)

No.	Table No.	Name of dye (with manufacturer's initials)	
960	V	Tinon Brilliant Green B2F-F	(Gy)
960	V	Tinon Brilliant Green BFP	(Gy)
975	V	Tinon Brilliant Green 2GF-F	(Gy)
40	I	Tinon Brilliant Orange GK-F	(Gy)
45	I	Tinon Brilliant Orange RK-F	(Gy)
335	II	Tinon Brilliant Pink G-F	(Gy)
495	II	Tinon Brilliant Pink 2R-F	(Gy)
1440	VI	Tinon Brown 3B-F	(Gy)
1375	VI	Tinon Brown BG-F	(Gy)
1295	VI	Tinon Brown BR-F	(Gy)
1275	VI	Tinon Brown 2BR-F	(Gy)
1325	VI	Tinon Brown GR-F	(Gy)
1390	VI	Tinon Brown RV-F	(Gy)
250	II	Tinon Copper Red R-F	(Gy)
630	IV	Tinon Dark Blue BO-F	(Gy)
630	IV	Tinon Dark Blue BOR	(Gy)
630	IV	Tinon Dark Blue MB-F	(Gy)
1515	VII	Tinon Direct Black DRB-F	(Gy)
1535	VII	Tinon Direct Black 2G-F	(Gy)
10	I	Tinon Golden Orange G-F	(Gy)
175	I	Tinon Golden Orange 3G-F	(Gy)
185	I	Tinon Golden Orange 2GT	(Gy)
25	I	Tinon Golden Orange 2R-F	(Gy)
130	I	Tinon Golden Yellow GK	(Gy)
5	I	Tinon Golden Yellow RK-F	(Gy)
30	I	Tinon Golden Yellow GW-F	(Gy)
1210	V	Tinon Green 6G-F	(Gy)
1560	VII	Tinon Grey AC	(Gy)
1785	VII	Tinon Grey BG-F	(Gy)
1750	VII	Tinon Grey 3G-F	(Gy)
1645	VII	Tinon Grey 2GR-F	(Gy)
1165	V	Tinon Khaki GG-F	(Gy)
1080	V	Tinon Khaki GR	(Gy)
775	IV	Tinon Navy Blue RA-F	(Gy)
1045	V	Tinon Olive B-F	(Gy)
1060	V	Tinon Olive 2B-F	(Gy)
1050	V	Tinon Olive BG-F	(Gy)
1110	V	Tinon Olive B2G-F	(Gy)
1045	V	Tinon Olive BM	(Gy)
1080	V	Tinon Olive 2G-F	(Gy)
1160	V	Tinon Olive 2R-F	(Gy)
1205	V	Tinon Olive S-F	(Gy)
110	I	Tinon Orange 6R	(Gy)
20	I	Tinon Orange 8R-F	(Gy)
310	II	Tinon Red 2B-F	(Gy)
510	II	Tinon Red 4B-F	(Gy)
300	II	Tinon Red 6B-F	(Gy)
525	II	Tinon Red F2B-F	(Gy)
445	II	Tinon Red G	(Gy)
245	II	Tinon Red RK-F	(Gy)
1345	VI	Tinon Red Brown R-F	(Gy)
1480	VI	Tinon Red Brown 2RF	(Gy)
550	III	Tinon Violet 6B-F	(Gy)
570	III	Tinon Violet 2BW	(Gy)
575	III	Tinon Violet FFBN	(Gy)
555	III	Tinon Violet 2RB-F	(Gy)
560	III	Tinon Violet 4R-F	(Gy)
35	I	Tinon Yellow GC	(Gy)
145	I	Tinon Yellow 5GK	(Gy)
210	I	Tinon Yellow GK-F	(Gy)
230	I	Tinon Yellow 2GK-F	(Gy)
65	I	Tinon Yellow GN-F	(Gy)
105	I	Tinon Yellow 2GR	(Gy)
225	I	Tinon Yellow 2GW	(Gy)
90	I	Tinon Yellow LGR-F	(Gy)
115	I	Tinon Yellow 3R-F	(Gy)
1340	VI	Tinon Yellow Brown G-F	(Gy)

No.	Colour index	Dye	Alkaline hydrosulphite	Acid hydrosulphite	Nitric acid	Sulphuric acid	Acid permanganate

No.	Colour index	Dye	Alkaline hydrosulphite	Acid hydrosulphite	Nitric acid	Sulphuric acid	Acid permanganate

No.	Colour index	Dye	Alkaline hydrosulphite	Acid hydrosulphite	Nitric acid	Sulphuric acid	Acid permanganate

No.	Colour index	Dye	Alkaline hydrosulphite	Acid hydrosulphite	Nitric acid	Sulphuric acid	Acid permanganate

MADE IN GREAT BRITAIN